Managing Your Hearing Loss
Impairment to Empowerment

Comments on Managing Your Hearing Loss: Impairment to Empowerment

'A very useful publication for the deaf and anyone who wishes to improve their knowledge on audiological rehabilitation.' *Peter Cross, Clinical Physiologist*

'It was a pleasure to read ... I am sure it will fill a niche in the market for people who have a hearing loss.' *Keith N Dunmore, Audiology Service Manager*

'An excellent highly readable book packed full of useful information.'
Sherif Habashi, ENT Consultant

'I think their book is a brilliant idea and will obviously be extremely useful to a lot of people.' *Gordon Hickish, General Practitioner*

'This book effectively brings all relevant information up to date within the new millennium ... I regard this book as being well conceived, easy to read and a nourishing guide for people with an acquired hearing loss ... a beneficial tool for related professionals ... and would recommend it for the shelves of any library.'
Bert Smale, Chairman of Teachers of Lipreading to Adults

'Congratulations to the authors. It is well written, concise, and a manual for referring to from time to time.' *Elizabeth Ward, Hearing Therapist*

Managing Your Hearing Loss
Impairment to Empowerment

Bunty Levene and Val Tait

Hearing Concern

Published by Hearing Concern
95 Gray's Inn Road
London WC1X 8TX
Tel: 020 7440 9871
Fax: 020 7440 9872
Email: info@hearingconcern.org.uk
Website: www.hearingconcern.org.uk
from whom further copies and a full publications list are available.

Hearing Concern is a Registered Charity no. 1094497 and
Company Limited by Guarantee no. 4466960

First published 2005
© 2005 Bunty Levene and Valerie Tait/Hearing Concern

ISBN 10: 0–9551365–0–4
ISBN 13: 978–0–9551365–0–4

British Library Cataloguing in Publication data
A catalogue record for this book is available from the British Library

Edited and indexed by Michèle Clarke
Illustrations by David Woodroffe

Designed and produced by Sandie Boccacci
Set in 10/13pt Stone Sans
Printed and bound in the United Kingdom by
The Basingstoke Press Limited

Contents

Acknowledgements

It is impossible to thank all those who helped us with our book. Many people have made valuable contributions for which we are grateful. Thank you.

In particular we should like to thank our husbands, Norman and Philip, for their encouragement and understanding while we did our research and writing. Their intelligent comments helped us to decide what to include. They knew why we felt it was so important to write the book and therefore tolerated our long hours working in the library and at the computer.

Thanks are due to Ross Trotter who has been a diligent editor and kind friend. He has generously allowed us to draw on his wide-ranging technical knowledge and on his personal experience of deafness. Ross suddenly lost all his hearing when he was 15 years old from meningitis. Without him this self-help book could not have been written.

We should also like to thank the members of Bunty's lipreading classes in north London for their suggestions for Chapter 22 entitled *Solutions for unanticipated situations*.

Thanks are due also from the authors and Hearing Concern to the following people who read the manuscript and made valuable comments: Peter Cross, Keith Dunmore, Sherif Habashi, Gordon Hickish, Bert Smale and Elizabeth Ward.

Finally, thank you to the staff of Hearing Concern, whose enthusiasm and support have been invaluable.

The Speech Banana figure is modified courtesy of R. McCall *Hearing loss: a guide to self-help*.

Foreword

I am delighted to have been asked to introduce this excellent self-help book for hard of hearing people. In my work with charities, I find many examples of the human spirit overcoming personal difficulties, but my admiration goes particularly to those who give freely of their own experiences so that their knowledge can benefit others.

The authors' intimate understanding of living with hearing loss gives a truly original insight into the world of the hard of hearing. Explanations of hearing loss and remedial treatment are followed by a host of invaluable tips, tricks and tactics to overcome daily problems. This very practical book is full of examples of typically difficult situations that often confront hard of hearing people and of countless new ways of thinking to help prepare and cope. Each negative situation is countered with a positive way to respond and we learn not only how to come to terms with hearing loss but how it can nurture new interests and fulfilments.

I have learnt so much from this book's honest, down-to-earth approach to managing human problems that I feel it will have a positive impact on any reader. I congratulate the authors on their balanced and entertaining guide to such an important subject. This is a manual for leading a healthy and rewarding life and I am sure it will bring confidence and hope to many hard of hearing people.

Introduction

This book is intended to provide some down-to-earth solutions for people who have lost all, most, or some of their useful hearing. For them lipreading and some form of amplification for hearing speech and warning noises is of vital importance, to ensure that they continue to experience the sense of being connected to the world.

The inspiration for writing this book came when we realised that our different experiences of hearing loss had benefited us in our work as Hearing Therapists and lipreading teachers, because we were both in a rare position to support the people with whom we were working. Bunty's husband was born with a hearing loss and is reliant on two powerful hearing aids and lipreading for understanding speech; also both her maternal grandparents were deaf. Val comes from a long line of deaf people and is deaf herself.

Between us we have, over a quarter of a century, devised many handouts for our patients to take away and learn from. For example, a diagram showing the frequency components of English speech sounds has proved very popular to illustrate the effects of a hearing loss. This handout is particularly useful when we ask the question, 'Have you found that it is easier to understand someone when you can see their face?' The answer has often been, 'Yes'. We then proceed to explain why this happens, by relating the result of the patient's hearing test (audiogram) to the speech sounds they cannot hear and to those which are visible on the face (see Chapter 2 on Understanding your hearing test and Chapter 7 on Lipreading).

This book focuses mainly on the social model of disability, which views the difficulties experienced by disabled people as the results of societal influences. These create the barriers that prevent disabled people taking part on an equal basis with non-disabled people. Incorrect perceptions and ignorance about hearing loss are the subjects of Chapter 3. Lack of opportunities in employment and education are two areas where these perceptions cause problems and they are the focus of Chapters 15 and 17. The emphasis in the social model is not on 'curing' the condition or illness but on educating people differently in the way that they regard disability, rather than looking for problems.

The medical model on the other hand is focused on correcting a defect by medical intervention, and pronounces that it is the individual's illness or disability that causes the problem and therefore the disabled person has to adapt to fit into the world as it is. It creates a cycle of dependency and exclusion, which is difficult to break. Hence the real reason for writing this book is to break this circle and provide some useful tactics for managing better.

It is often the simple changes that make the most difference to managing a hearing loss. The suggestion of placing a doily, or a small tissue, between a cup and a saucer to prevent the inevitable clash of crockery on crockery is frequently greeted with, 'What a good idea!' We then go on to explain that many environmental sounds are louder than speech sounds, and if, for example, the person you are with asks you a question such as, 'Would you like a piece of shortbread or a piece of cake?', you may not understand them because, just as they start to speak, you put your cup down in order to concentrate better, and the sound of your cup will have been louder than the initial consonants of 'shortbread' and 'piece of cake'. Whereas if you had placed a doily between the cup and saucer there would have been no sound. We suggest you try this simple tip for yourself and find out what a difference it makes (see Chapter 19). If you are profoundly deaf and rely totally on lipreading for communication, then we recommend that you sit with your back to the light in order to facilitate lipreading –

again do try this for yourself and see the result. These practical suggestions and many, many more are in this book.

We have not attempted to write in depth about tinnitus, Ménière's disease, sign language or the technical aspects of cochlear implants and hearing aids. Nor have we attempted to give you reasons why you have lost all or some of your hearing. Instead we want this book to be useful and supportive for those of you who have felt, and perhaps still feel, that maybe it is your fault that other people's speech seems distorted or that you do not always hear the door bell. You remember being able to understand your family, friends and colleagues, and now you feel very frustrated that sometimes they sound like parrots or Mickey Mouse. You may also feel angry and embarrassed when someone looks irritated or alerts you in an almost aggressive way because you simply have not heard the door or telephone bell. It was not that you ignored the sound, you just did not hear it!

You may feel as though you have lost some part of yourself and in Chapter 4 we look at this experience in more detail and offer some solutions for coping with these unwelcome emotions. Also you may not understand why this has happened, so in Chapter 1 we explain how you hear and why this unwanted situation has occurred.

If, as you are reading this book, you come across a term you do not understand, look it up in the Glossary (Appendix 3) where you will find an explanation.

The World Health Organisation (WHO) has a strategic target to eliminate 50% of avoidable hearing loss by the year 2010 through appropriate preventative and rehabilitative measures, acknowledging that hearing loss is an international concern affecting all races and ages. It has been ever thus and this book comes from a real belief that, by being enabled, informed and empowered, you will manage better. This book may not have all the answers but we hope it will point you in the right direction. After you have read it, we hope you may feel able to manage your hearing loss rather than feel as if it is managing you, and that your hearing loss may change from something that appears to dominate your life to something peripheral.

Note that any terms you may not understand in the text are defined and explained further in the Glossary (Appendix 3).

Chapter 1

The ear and how it works

What diamonds are equal to my eyes;
What labyrinths to my ears;
What gates of ivory, or ruby leaves
To the double portal of my lips and teeth?

Thomas Traherne, *Centuries*

When we set out to write this book, we were surprised at how many of our patients asked us to include a chapter about how the ear works. Any basic Ear, Nose and Throat (ENT) textbook can give you a highly detailed anatomical description of the ear. By way of contrast, this chapter sets out to describe the ear for readers who do not have medical training.

Most people have two ears. We cannot see our own ears, unless we look in the mirror, and most of the time we ignore them – unless we are putting on our glasses or fastening our earrings. The only other time we consider our ears is when they cause us any trouble.

Although we take our ears for granted, they are continuously receiving sound, even when we are asleep. Much of the information we receive about the world around us comes to us via our ears. Amongst other things, our ears and brain tell us:

◆ what sounds are around us;
◆ where we are;
◆ where the sounds that we hear are coming from;
◆ whether the sounds are dangerous, neutral or friendly;
◆ whether we need more information about a sound, or whether we can ignore it;
◆ whether it is a familiar sound or a new sound;
◆ whether we can go on sleeping or whether we should wake up;
◆ whether the person speaking to us is speaking our own language or a foreign language;
◆ whether the person speaking to us via the telephone is a friend or a stranger;
◆ whether the car is running properly or whether there is something wrong with the engine.

Our ears are extremely sophisticated and sensitive and the list above covers only a small number of sounds that we can identify or distinguish between. To summarise, our ears can:

◆ identify – who or what is making the noise?
◆ distinguish and categorise – which one of a group, e.g. which person, out of all the people we know, is speaking?
◆ warn – that noise is dangerous, watch out! take action!
◆ quantify – how loud is that noise?
◆ qualify – pitch, e.g. is it a high-pitched noise (like birdsong) or a low-pitched noise (like a rumble of thunder)?
◆ filter – ignore any sounds that we deem irrelevant and pick out important sounds.

How does the ear work?

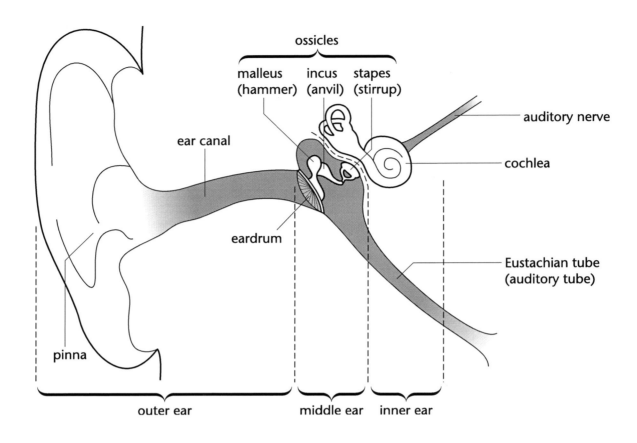

This is a simplified description of how sound passes from the ear to the brain. The words/phrases in bold show the path through the ear. The words in brackets and italics give the medical terminology, so that you will know what the doctor is talking about if he uses these words instead of the everyday ones!

The ear is divided into three sections:

◆   the outer ear
◆   the middle ear
◆   the inner ear.

The outer ear

Sound enters the outer ear by means of the **pinna**. The **pinna** is stiffened by cartilage and is shaped the way it is to catch sound and channel it down the **ear canal** (*external auditory meatus*). We have two ears so that we can tell from which direction a sound is coming. Those of you who have hearing in only one ear will know how difficult it is to identify correctly where sound is coming from. (Those of you who have a hearing loss in both ears but only wear a hearing aid in one ear may have noticed a similar problem.) At the end of the **ear canal** is the **eardrum** (*tympanic membrane*).

Outer ear: pinna → ear canal → eardrum →

The middle ear (tympanic cavity)

The middle ear passes sound from the **eardrum** to the **cochlea** by means of the **ossicles**. The **ossicles** are a chain of three small bones (called the *malleus*, the *incus* and the *stapes*[1]) that transmit vibrations from the **eardrum** to the **cochlea** in the inner ear.

The middle ear also contains the opening of the **Eustachian tube** (*auditory tube*) – this leads from the front of the middle ear cavity to the back of the nose. It is necessary to keep the pressure in the middle ear the same as that of the outside world. It is the Eustachian tube that goes 'pop' whenever you go somewhere very high (such as in an aeroplane) or very low (such as a fast-descending lift). On the London Underground any popping is due to pressure caused by the trains' speed rather than the depth.

Middle ear: → ossicles (*malleus + incus + stapes*) → cochlea

The inner ear

The **stapes** is attached to the **cochlea**, which looks like a coiled shell. The **cochlea** is extremely complex for such a tiny organ (it is about the size of a little fingernail) and transmits sound to the auditory nerve (the *VIIIth nerve*). The cochlea is filled with fluid (rather similar to spinal fluid). In the fluid are thousands of tiny, hair-like cells. As sound passes through the cochlea, the hair cells move. As they move, signals are transmitted to the auditory nerve, which in turn, carries messages to the brain. In this way sound is transformed from a mechanical stimulation to an electrical one. The brain identifies the sound and decides on a response.

Inner ear: → cochlea → auditory nerve → brain

What can go wrong?

When you see how many different parts make up the ear, and when you realise how delicate the ear is, it is a wonder that anybody's ears work correctly at all! When doctors talk about hearing loss, they usually speak of two different kinds:

◆ conductive deafness
◆ sensorineural (cochlear and/or nerve) deafness.

Conductive deafness

Conductive deafness occurs when anything goes wrong with the outer and middle ear (the mechanical parts of the ear) – the pinna, the ear canal, the eardrum, or the ossicles. The commonest cause is accumulated wax blocking the ear canal. Conductive hearing loss makes everything sound very quiet, but it does not make things sound distorted. Someone who has a conductive hearing loss and wears a hearing aid, will probably be delighted with what they hear – nice, clear sound. A person with a conductive hearing loss may speak in a quiet voice. They may be able to hear better in noisy surroundings. The good news about conductive hearing loss is a surgical operation may be available to improve hearing. Please note that we are not saying that all conductive hearing loss is curable. Each case must be decided on its own merits by someone properly qualified to do so.

'Conductive hearing loss can almost always be restored to some degree, if not completely' (Polsdorfer, 2002 – see Appendix 2 Further Reading for more details).

It is not possible to list all the things that can go wrong with people's hearing here.

All we have tried to do here is to list some of the common problems that can cause conductive hearing loss.

Common problems with the ear canal

Wax (*cerumen*) Normal healthy ears should have wax in them. Wax is nature's way of keeping the ear clean and healthy. Wax is secreted as a fluid by glands in the outer third of the ear canal. As it dries it becomes sticky, trapping dust, bacteria and other undesirable foreign bodies. Under natural circumstances, the surface wax finally dries and disappears imperceptibly as a fine powder. Frequent washing, or swimming, interferes with this drying process and may lead to troublesome accumulation of wax. Unfortunately a hearing aid can have a similar effect. A problem arises when the ear canal becomes blocked with hardened wax (this is often a dark colour). **Do not try to remove wax with a cotton bud** – this may have the effect of pushing the wax further down the ear canal and thus damage the eardrum. If you think your ears are blocked with wax, see your GP who will advise you. Do not poke or prod your ears and never put anything down them unless recommended to do so by a doctor. Prescribed eardrops and syringing, or suction, often remove wax. A suitably (or properly) qualified person should always carry out these procedures. The ear canal is self-cleaning and should require no intervention. The cells lining it grow continually from the middle of the eardrum and migrate centrifugally to the edge of the drum and then outwards along the canal to the pinna – at the rate of about 0.5 mm per day. The ear canals are thus normally kept immaculately clean.

Infection (*otitis externa*) The ear canal can become infected. You may feel pain and/or itching. If the infection blocks the ear, you will have difficulty hearing and you may have temporary ringing in the ears (*tinnitus*). See your GP. Infections are often cleared up by prescribed eardrops.

Osteomata (*exostoses*) Small, bony growths commonly found in the ears of those who enjoy swimming in cold water. They seldom cause any problems and, although they can be removed by surgery, this is rarely necessary.

Common problems with the eardrum

Perforation (hole in the eardrum) Perforation is mainly caused by middle ear infection but can also be caused by the ear being poked with a sharp object (e.g. a cotton bud!); by sudden changes in pressure (e.g. diving); by excessively loud noise (e.g. an explosion), or by trauma (e.g. a blow to the head). The eardrum will often heal on its own. If it does not do so, a surgeon might perform a fascial graft (*myringoplasty*).

Commom problems with the ossicles

Otosclerosis This is usually a hereditary problem more common in women than in men. It often appears when a person is in their twenties or thirties and typically affects both ears. A spongy-looking growth (it is in fact new bone) forms on the ossicles, especially the stapes. This means that they cannot move so freely and the vibrations from sound are hindered from passing from the middle ear to the cochlea. Otosclerosis can sometimes spread to the cochlea as well. When this happens, sensorineural hearing loss can occur. An operation called a *stapedectomy* can sometimes be performed. During this operation part of the stapes is removed and replaced by an artificial prosthesis.

Trauma A blow to the head can damage the ossicles, thus preventing sound passing from the eardrum to the cochlea.

Other important causes of conductive deafness

Chronic suppurative otitis media Chronic ear infection may lead to perforation of the eardrum and erosion or immobility of the ossicles resulting in conductive deafness.

Tympanosclerosis Calcium deposits within the eardrum or around the ossicles can develop following middle ear infection. These can dampen the vibrations of the eardrum and ossicles.

Otitis media with effusion (glue ear) An obstruction or poorly functioning Eustachian tube leads to a low pressure in the middle ear, which, if long standing, leads to fluid being drawn into the middle ear. This is an extremely common cause of conductive deafness in children but can also occur in adults.

Sensorineural deafness

Sensorineural hearing loss occurs when anything goes wrong with the cochlea or auditory nerve, which carries the signals picked up by the cochlea to the brain. Sensorineural hearing loss makes everything sound quieter and distorted. Someone who has a sensorineural hearing loss may speak in a loud voice and have difficulty hearing if there is background noise. Hearing aids may help the person with nerve deafness to hear better, but there may always be a lack of clarity, which can be distressing. The hearing aid is not always to blame: it is the nature of the hearing loss that is often the problem. Most sensorineural hearing loss is caused by wear and tear to the hair cells in the cochlea. The place in the cochlea where the hair cells have been damaged indicates which sounds the person will have difficulty hearing. The number of hair cells destroyed will indicate how great the hearing loss is. The larger the number of hair cells destroyed, the greater the hearing loss. Sensorineural hearing loss is inoperable. This is because it has not been possible so far to replace damaged cochlear hair cells. If your hearing loss in one ear becomes very severe and is caused by hair cell damage to the cochlea, you may be offered a cochlear implant. This is not a replacement ear, but rather a sophisticated form of hearing aid.

'Sensory and neural hearing loss, on the other hand, cannot readily be cured. Fortunately it is not often complete, so that hearing aids can fill the deficit' (Polsdorfer, 2002). Some kinds of sensorineural hearing loss are listed below.

Common problems with the cochlea

Age-related hearing loss (*presbyacusis*) As we get older, parts of the body begin to wear out. Some people find that they need to wear glasses, or have false teeth, or walk with a stick, or use a hearing aid. The hair cells in the cochlea are affected by the wear and tear of everyday life. Age-related hearing loss can worsen with age. Elderly patients often joke, 'Don't get old,' to which the only reply is, 'Well, I don't think much of the alternative!'

Ménière's disease This is the name given to a condition affecting both the semicircular canals (the organ of balance) and the cochlea in the ear. People with Ménière's have episodes when they experience temporary deafness, dizziness (*vertigo*) and noises in the ear (*tinnitus*). In between episodes they are quite well. One or both ears may be affected. Sometimes, Ménière's goes into remission so that the person will be free of episodes for months or even years. The hearing is gradually reduced in the affected ear over a period of time.

Familial/genetic causes Inheriting faulty genes from one or both parents may result in sensorineural deafness. This may present in early adult life with a progressive hearing loss that affects the mid frequencies more than the lower and higher ones.

Congenital Around 1 in 1000 babies are born with sensorineural deafness. This may be due to faulty genes or damage in the womb from infection, such as rubella, but this is now rare.

Noise-induced hearing loss (NIHL) This is a condition often found in people who are exposed to very loud sounds on a regular basis. Many patients that we see who have this problem have worked in factories with noisy machinery, been in the armed forces, used guns, visited pop concerts or worked as musicians. Current legislation insists that ear protection is provided by employers for any employees exposed to high levels of sound. There is not, at present, any legal requirement for protection to be offered to people who are exposed to loud sound during leisure activities. This means that, if you are someone who operates a pneumatic drill, you will be issued with ear protection by your employer. On the other hand, if, on your day off, you visit a music festival, you will not usually be offered any ear protection at all.

So, which sounds are safe? As a general guideline, repeated exposure to sounds of between 80 and 90 decibels can lead to noise-induced hearing loss. How loud is sound? This table will give you an approximate idea of how much sound you are exposing your ears to.

Levels of sound

Decibels	Sound
30	gentle whisper
35	clock ticking in a quiet room
40	quiet office
50	ordinary conversation
60	average television
70	traffic, noisy restaurant
80	factory, heavy traffic, loud alarm clock
90	noisy party chatter, loud lawnmower
100	pneumatic drill
120	thunder
140	aeroplane

Be sensible, you have only one pair of ears: replacements are not available. If you are offered ear protection, wear it! If you have a noisy hobby, wear ear protection.[2]

Medicines that affect the ears (*ototoxic drugs*) High doses of some medication can affect the hearing. Common examples of this are aspirin, gentamicin and quinine. Don't stop or change your medicine without your doctor's advice. It is unlikely that the low-dose aspirin taken for heart problems would affect hearing.

Common problems that can also affect the auditory nerve

Acoustic neuroma (*vestibular schwannoma*) This is a benign tumour that forms on the auditory nerve. An unexplained sensorineural hearing loss in one ear accompanied by such symptoms as tinnitus, numbness in one side of the face or problems with the eyesight in one eye may indicate an acoustic neuroma. An operation can be performed to remove it.

Sometimes it is not possible to diagnose exactly what has caused a person's hearing loss. Here is a case history to illustrate the point.

Walter is a 70-year-old man with hearing loss in both ears. As a child, he suffered from repeated ear infections, which caused damage to both his eardrums. As a teenager he went into the Air Force and served an apprenticeship learning how to repair aircraft engines. Those were the days before ear protection was considered necessary. He started wearing hearing aids in his late twenties. In his forties he developed meningitis, probably as a result of a neglected ear infection. His mother was also very deaf. He is now profoundly deaf. What caused his deafness?

- ◆ **Family history** – *was it a hereditary problem? (conductive or sensorineural)*
- ◆ **Ear infection** - *repeated ear infections would have scarred the eardrums and affected his hearing (conductive)*
- ◆ **NIHL** – *it is likely that the noise from the plane engines also caused damage (sensorineural)*
- ◆ **Meningitis** – *this could have further damaged his hearing (sensorineural)*
- ◆ **Presbyacusis** - *Walter is now 70. Old age may well have made a contribution to his hearing difficulties (sensorineural)*

Any combination of these factors or all of them could have caused Walter's problems. It is now impossible to say which problem made the biggest difference. Antibiotics in childhood (which are now readily available) and ear protection in adulthood might have made a considerable difference to Walter's life. He might now have only a mild or moderate hearing loss and be coping very well with just one hearing aid.

Stroke People who have had a stroke or other health problems such as multiple sclerosis may find that their ability to hear is affected as well.

Earache (*otalgia*)

Earache can be caused by a variety of things such as infection, impacted wax or a foreign body. It can also be caused by things that are nothing to do with the ear at all! This is called referred pain and can be caused by having trouble with impacted teeth, having recently had a tonsillectomy, or even shingles (*herpes zoster*). If you have a persistent earache, do not try to guess what is wrong with you and treat it yourself, visit your GP. We know a lady who was troubled with earache for some weeks until it was cured by her dentist who discovered that she had an impacted wisdom tooth. Once the tooth was removed, the earache ceased completely!

Doctors cannot always tell why people have a hearing problem but there are some precautions that people can take:
- ◆ Wear ear protection if you work in a noisy place, have a noisy hobby, or use noisy tools like petrol hedge trimmers, strimmers and garden mowers.
- ◆ If you enjoy listening to music, do not turn the volume up above 80 dB.
- ◆ Never neglect an ear infection – go to the doctor at once if you have persistent earache.
- ◆ Keep water out of your eardrums if you have a history of ear infections by wearing swim plugs when swimming and when in the shower or washing your hair, but remember that ear plugs can encourage wax impaction.
- ◆ Do not put anything down your ears, unless advised to do so by the doctor.
- ◆ Do not poke your ears with anything; not even a cotton bud.

◆ If you think your ears are blocked with wax, see your GP. Do not attempt to treat yourself.

◆ Take care of your ears!

Notes

1 They are so called because of their shape. *Malleus* is the Latin word for a hammer – the bone is hammer shaped. *Incus* is the Latin word for an anvil. *Stapes* is the Latin word for a stirrup.

2 Specialised ear protection is available for musicians, enabling them to block out excessive sound.

Chapter 2

Understanding your hearing test

What makes you think you have a hearing loss?

Since most of us are not doctors, we have to use common sense to tell us when we think that our body is not working properly. Perhaps we might have a cough or a pain that gives us the hint to go to our GP. What happens with our ears? Some of the common things that you might notice if you have a hearing loss are:

◆ **Family and friends complain that you have the television on far too loud.**
   A: 'Turn that down, mother, please, it's deafening. Haven't the neighbours complained?'
   B: 'Yes they're always complaining. But it doesn't sound loud to me. I can only just hear it.'

◆ **You don't hear the doorbell like you used to.**
   X: 'I called on Tuesday afternoon but you were out.'
   Y: 'No I was in all day. Did you ring the doorbell?'
   X: 'Yes, several times and I used the knocker.'

◆ **You have problems using the telephone.**
   N: 'Charles, it's Nigel here.'
   C: 'Sorry, who is it?'
   N: 'It's Nigel, your solicitor. I'm telephoning about your conveyancing.'
   C: 'Oh, Nigel, yes. What did you want to talk to me about?'
   N: 'About your new house.'
   C: 'Say that again.'
   N: 'Look, I'll write.'

◆ **You find it difficult to hear in background noise.**
   E: 'Can you pick up the children from school tomorrow?' (At the same time as the TV is stating, 'And now the weather forecast.')
   F: 'I think it will be fine.'
   E: 'Was that 'yes' or 'no'?' ((TV: 'Temperatures tomorrow will reach …')
   F: 'Sorry, what did you say? I can't hear you and the television together!'

◆ **You can no longer hear a familiar sound such as your clock ticking.**
   V: 'That clock has stopped.'
   P: 'What makes you think that? The second hand is still moving.'
   V: 'Well, I can't hear it tick!'
   P: 'I can hear it ticking from where I'm standing and I'm further away from it than you are. It's really loud.'

What should you do next?

The next thing to do is to go and see your GP. He/she will probably examine your ears and check them for wax and infection. If your ears seem clear and there are no other obvious causes of hearing loss, he will refer you to your nearest ENT (or Head and Neck) Consultant. Quite a few GPs have their own audiometers and may arrange an initial audiogram within the practice. Many areas operate a Direct referral scheme for elderly patients who require a hearing aid. This would mean that they would be referred directly to an Audiology Department. An Audiologist would then take their history and examine their ears.

GP → ENT/Head and Neck Consultant → Audiologist → Hearing Therapist

The consultant will *examine* your ears. He/she too is checking for things like wax, infection and perforated eardrums and making sure that all the parts of the ear that are visible are healthy and in working order.

During the consultation, the specialist will *take a history*. The kinds of things asked include:

◆ When did you first notice you had a problem? How long have you felt like this?
◆ Does anyone else in your family have a hearing loss? If so, do you know what caused it?
◆ Which ear is giving you trouble? Or is it both ears?
◆ Do your ears hurt?
◆ Have your ears been bleeding or discharging?
◆ Have you had any other symptoms, e.g. tinnitus (noises in the head or ears)?
◆ Have you recently had a bad cold or 'flu?
◆ Have you recently flown in an aeroplane or been diving?
◆ Have you banged your head?
◆ Do you have any other health problems?
◆ Are you taking any medicine either purchased over the counter or prescribed by a doctor?
◆ Has anything unusual happened lately?
◆ Why do you think that you cannot hear?
◆ Have you done any noisy work or military service?
◆ Have you listened to loud music or used power tools?

Try to make your answers as clear as you can. If, for example, you do take medicine, it is helpful if you can tell the doctor exactly what you take. Just telling him/her that you are taking 'those little yellow pills' is not very useful. It is very helpful if you answer the question 'Why do you think that you cannot hear?' with some examples, e.g. 'Everyone says that I have the television on much too loudly.'

You may then be asked to listen to the sound that a tuning fork makes. The doctor strikes the tuning fork on a hard object and then places it against your head. If it is placed on your forehead you will be asked which ear you hear the sound in. This test is known as the *Weber test*. In the *Rinne test*, the tuning fork is held first to the side of the ear and then, when the sound can no longer be heard, applied to the bone behind the ear. These tests can give the doctor some indication as to whether you have a sensorineural or a conductive hearing loss.

Next you may be sent to the Audiology Department for some diagnostic tests. There are a whole variety of tests, which *audiologists* use. The doctor will only request those that are necessary to make a diagnosis in your case. Some of the tests can be quite time consuming and you do not want to waste your time having unnecessary tests done.

Once the tests are done, the Audiologist sends the results to the doctor. Often this is all done on the same day, so that you go straight back to the doctor for the results. The doctor interprets the results of the test and any other information about you. This is the evidence that the *diagnosis* is based on. All this evidence will tell the doctor things such as what has caused your hearing loss, the name of the condition that you have, and what the future may hold for your hearing (*prognosis*). For example, the doctor may find that you have a severe unilateral sensorineural hearing loss caused by *infectious parotitis*. Translated into everyday language this means that you have nerve deafness in one ear following mumps and you will have difficulty hearing sounds quieter than 70 dB in that ear. The other ear is all right.

How does all this apply to me?

The test that probably tells the doctor the most about your hearing is the *pure tone audiogram* (*PTA*). At the end of this test, during which you listen to a variety of sounds at different pitches and volumes, the Audiologist will have produced a chart of your hearing called an *audiogram*. The audiogram shows the medical professionals exactly what you can hear. What does the chart mean?

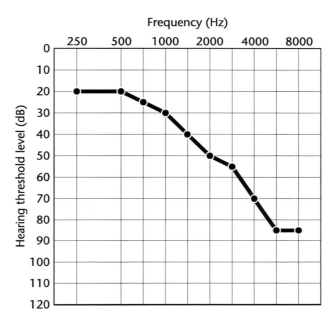

An audiogram is a graph. The *x* (horizontal) axis represents *frequency* (high or low pitch) and is measured in *hertz*. The *y* (vertical) axis represents *volume* (loudness) and is measured in *decibels* (dB). The '0' (nought) line on the horizontal axis represents sound that is at the equivalent volume of a whisper in a quiet room. The points plotted with an 'O' represent the sounds heard by the right ear. The points plotted with an 'X' represent the sounds heard by the left ear. People with unimpaired hearing can hear sounds between 0 (nought) and 20 dB. Anyone with hearing below those levels may have a hearing loss. An audiogram shows what you can hear when you are not wearing hearing aids of any kind.

Different kinds of hearing loss have differently shaped audiograms. The one shown above indicates moderate old age deafness (*presbyacusis*). People with presbyacusis have bilateral sensorineural (nerve) deafness. The hair cells in the cochlea have become worn with age thus causing the sensorineural loss, and both ears are the same age, hence bilateral. The hearing in the high frequencies generally wears out first, and so the graph slopes down from left to right. The person would hear low-pitched sounds, like traffic, loud and clear, but have problems with high-pitched noises, such as bird-song. This also explains why elderly people often have problems hearing what children say but can hear men's voices much more clearly. Children often have high-pitched squeaky voices, while men usually have deeper voices.

What does moderate mean? The four terms *mild, moderate, severe* and *profound* have a precise definition in audiology:

◆ *mild* means that the person is unable to hear sounds between 20 dB and 40 dB;
◆ *moderate* means that the person is unable to hear sounds between 41 dB and 70 dB;
◆ *severe* means that the person is unable to hear sounds between 71 dB and 95 dB;
◆ *profound* means that the person is unable to hear sounds louder than 95 dB.

A 'dead ear' means that the Audiologist has been unable to measure any hearing in that ear. A person with a 'dead ear' will be will not be helped by a hearing aid in that ear.

What does all this mean in practical terms?

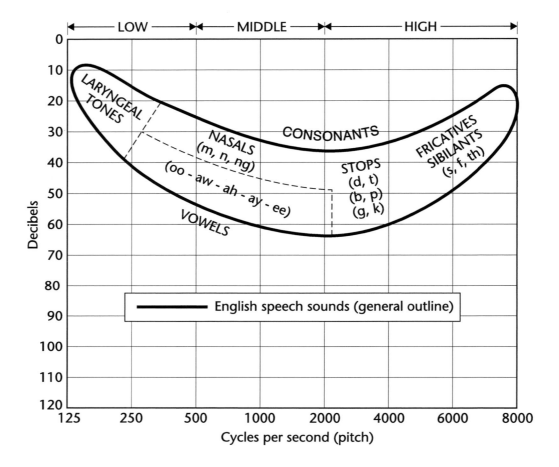

This diagram is known, because of its shape, as the 'speech banana'. It simply shows the places on an audiogram where the different speech sounds can be found. Notice that the sounds such as 'sh', 'th', 'f' and 'v' are high frequency sounds. They are also very quiet sounds (10–30 dB). That means that they would be difficult to hear for anyone who has a high frequency hearing loss (but easier to hear for anyone who has a low frequency hearing loss). Vowel sounds such as 'oo', 'aw' and 'ee' are more middle frequency sounds and they are much louder sounds too (40–60 dB). That would mean that anyone with a high frequency hearing loss would stand a better chance of hearing them.

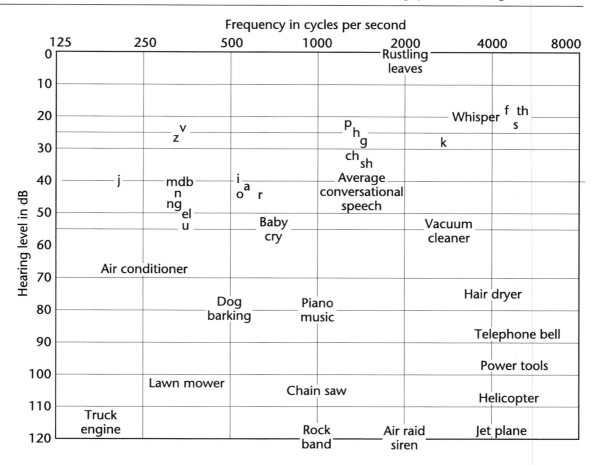

Sometimes pictures speak more clearly than words. This diagram shows what kind of sounds you can expect to hear at different volumes. A person with unimpaired hearing can hear a whisper in a quiet room. A person with a profound hearing loss will not be able to hear speech (which is around 60 dB) but may be able to hear a pneumatic drill (100 dB). This will give you some idea of the kinds of sounds you may be able to hear and the things that may give you problems.

Certain kinds of hearing loss may involve tinnitus (noises in the head or ears). While tinnitus is harmless in itself, it should always be mentioned to your consultant since treatment is available for it. (Ask to see your *Hearing Therapist* for further details.)

Once the doctor has made a diagnosis, the next step is to decide what can be done about it. In other words, are we looking at medication, operation, rehabilitation or a combination of the three? Hearing losses caused by infection or wax can often be sorted out by some form of medication. Some hearing losses, caused by things like otosclerosis, glue ear, chronic suppurative otitis media, may be improved by an operation. **Most people, however, will be offered some form of rehabilitation, for example hearing aids, lipreading, special equipment (e.g. flashing light doorbell), counselling or cochlear implants.** Audiologists and Hearing Therapists provide rehabilitation.

Understanding your diagnosis

Ring the words which apply to you:

1. Which ear?

Unilateral (one ear)   Right ear   Left ear   Bilateral (both ears)

2. Kind of deafness

Sensorineural deafness (nerve deafness)   Conductive deafness

Mixed deafness (sensorineural and conductive)

3. Degree of deafness

Mild (20–40 dB)   Moderate (41–70 dB)   Profound (95+ dB)

Severe (71–95 dB)

4. Cause

- Acoustic neuroma (benign tumour of the auditory nerve)
- Atresia (closure of the ear canal)
- Barotrauma (caused by sudden changes in pressure, e.g. diving)
- Infection
- Inherited hearing loss
- Ménière's disease
- Meningitis
- Noise-induced hearing loss (NIHL)
- Osteomata or exotoses (bony growth in the ear canal)
- Otosclerosis
- Ototoxic drugs
- Perforation (hole in the eardrum)
- Presbyacusis (old age)
- Trauma
- Unknown
- Virus
- Wax (cerumen)
- Other causes

5. What the doctor has recommended

- Medication
- Operation
- Hearing aid(s)
- Cochlear implant(s)
- Lipreading
- British Sign Language
- Special equipment
- Hearing therapy
- Tinnitus management

6. To find out more about your hearing loss, contact one or more of the following:

- Your local library
- The internet – many conditions have their own website
- A national charity – either a general one, for example Hearing Concern or the RNID, or a specific one, for example The Ménière's Society (see Appendix 1)
- A local charity or support group
- Your local lipreading class
- Your local Hearing Therapist (based at the hospital's Audiology Department)
- A friend or relative with the same, or similar, problems.

Do not be afraid to ask questions of your local GP, ENT consultant, Audiologist, Lipreading Teacher or Hearing Therapist.

Chapter 3

Experiencing a quiet world

> Hearing loss? Yes, loss is what we hear
> who are starting to go deaf. Loss
> trails a lot of weird puns in its wake, viz.
> Dad's a real prism of the Left –
> You'd like me to repeat that?
> THE SAD SURREALISM OF THE DEAF.
>
> Les A Murray, *Hearing Impairment*

So, what's it like being deaf?

We took the above quotation from a book of comic verse – that in itself tells you a great deal about how the world views deafness. It is hard to think of a convincingly funny poem about blindness (by contrast think of Milton's great tragic sonnet on his blindness), but deafness seems to most people to be a fair subject for jokes and humour. However, the poem is a good example of what conversation can sound like to a hard of hearing or deaf person.

- What the hearing person said was, 'The s**ad** sur**real**ism of the d**eaf**.'
- What the deaf person thought they heard was, 'D**ad**'s a **real** prism of th**e L**eft.'

That is the difficulty with most hearing loss: very few people hear nothing at all. Many people who are hard of hearing or deaf hear some sounds. What varies from person to person is how much they hear. It is confusing for both deaf and hearing people. The deaf person thinks they have heard what was said and answers accordingly. If they have misheard, their answers make no sense to the hearing person and both become increasingly frustrated as the conversation goes on. Hearing people can sometimes become angry. 'He heard the traffic, why can't he hear me? He does it deliberately.'

From the poem, it looks as if this deaf person has a high frequency sensorineural hearing loss. What is the evidence for that? A conductive hearing loss makes everything sound the same, just much quieter, whereas sensorineural (or nerve) deafness causes speech to sound quieter and distorted. If the deaf person had had a conductive loss he would just have needed the hearing person to speak up a bit! He can hear the vowels and has got most of those correct. Vowels are low frequency sounds and are louder than consonants. It is the consonant sounds that are giving him trouble; these are the high frequency sounds.

The poem is full of 'surreal' mistakes like this. If hearing people ever have this kind of conversation with a deaf person, they must be patient, and never feel that the deaf person's apparent obtuseness is deliberate.

This chapter is written so that hearing people can have some idea of what it is like to be hard of hearing or deaf and so that hard of hearing people reading it can say, 'Yes, that's what it's like! I thought I was the only one.'

Imagine a cold winter's day in a busy northern town. Imagine a hard of hearing woman sitting at a table by a window in the main library in the town. The man sitting opposite her is rapidly turning the pages of his book. In the street outside the window, a child is having a tantrum while his mother scolds him. The road is busy with a continuous stream of traffic. Directly outside the window is a tree. The branches are bare and filled with birds. They are all making quite a racket. One of the librarians is passing to and fro with a pile of books. The pile is too heavy for her and the books begin to slide. They all fall to the floor. She stoops to pick them up. Someone comes to help her. Everyone turns their head to watch – except for the deaf woman, quietly absorbed in her studies. Although she is wearing her hearing aids, the outside world only exists for her if she can see, feel, taste or touch it. When her eyes are fixed on her book and she is concentrating on her reading, she is unaware of the sound of pages being turned, a child screaming, traffic going past, birds singing and even books falling. As she reads, she taps her pencil against her teeth. The man sitting at the same table finds this irritating. She does not realise that the pencil makes a noise. She likes the reassurance that fidgeting gives her and does not even realise she is doing it. Fidgeting is her way of checking that the external world still exists. Hearing people do this by listening.

She is aware of the man sitting opposite her – how? When he sat down, he bumped into the table slightly and she felt it vibrate gently. He is a smoker and she is not, so she can smell the cigarette smoke that lingers on his clothes and his hair. She can also feel the draught caused by the pages of his book being turned.

Her peripheral vision is good. She can see further 'out of the corner of her eyes' than most hearing people. So she is vaguely aware of movement outside the window. She knows there is something going on, but it is not important enough for her to look out of the window. If she becomes bored with her studies, or if the movement becomes threatening or dangerous, she may stop and gaze for a while. She can 'tune out' unimportant movements, just as a hearing person may 'tune out' unimportant background sounds such as a ticking clock or a humming refrigerator.

Her concentration is excellent. Her hearing loss means that she is not so easily distracted as a hearing person. She feels comfortable with the written word. With a book or a magazine in her hand, she is the equal of a hearing person. If she enjoys reading, the world of books may become, for her, more comfortable and even more real than the world around her with its harsh and confusing sounds, its fractured and disjointed conversation, its impatient people. She often feels stupid when talking to people – she never feels stupid with a book.

> In a word, literature is my Utopia. Here I am not disenfranchised. No barrier of the senses shuts me out from my book-friends. They talk to me without embarrassment or awkwardness.'
>
> Helen Keller, *The Story Of My Life*

Research has shown that the ability to hear background sound is necessary to our psychological well-being. We need to know that the world around us is still there. What happens if you are unable to hear this comforting noise? Many hard of hearing or deaf people compensate for the lack of sound by creating their own contact with the world by touching it. They may jingle the coins in their trouser pocket, drum their fingers on the table, fidget with their hair, tap their feet or even tap their teeth with a pencil. This can be extremely irritating for their hearing friends, family and colleagues, but it is necessary for them.

Why do your pockets wear out so fast?

Are you afflicted with the deaf person's handbag (or pocket) syndrome? Many people with a hearing loss find shopping difficult. Shops are big noisy places with dreadful acoustics (lots of hard surfaces) and full of strangers whom it is difficult to lipread. The person at the till may be difficult to hear and impossible to lipread. How much money do you owe? You may not be able to see the figures on the till. So what do you do?

You estimate the amount needed and offer a banknote for more than that amount. You think you owe around £15, so you tender a £20 note. Terrific, problem solved! By the end of a busy week, your handbag (or pocket) weighs a great deal. One hard of hearing lady I know was once out shopping with her hearing husband and was asked by a local shopkeeper if she had any change. She said she thought she had. Her husband laughed – he knew she would have – and helped her turn out her handbag. She had £30 in coins in the bottom of the bag! The shopkeeper was delighted. She now empties her bag of change every night and puts the money in a jar. When the jar is full she treats herself to a bar of chocolate and banks the rest of the contents. Last time she emptied the jar, it held £90!

Why do you grin like the Cheshire Cat?

Everyone smiles. It is a well-known signal from one human being to another and as such is recognised by people all over the world. Many people who are deaf use smiling as a coping mechanism. When you have been listening and lipreading a complicated conversation for a long time, you can become fatigued and lose the thread of what is being talked about. For a while you can manage by looking alert and interested, and then the person you are listening to says, 'Well, what do you think?' What do you do? If you know the person well and feel comfortable with them, you might say, 'I'm sorry, I didn't quite catch that.' However, you might just look at them and smile brightly. This is usually quite effective. Unfortunately, smiling is sometimes inappropriate.

> A lipreading class member thought her hearing friend said, 'My mother is deaf.' And so smiled broadly and asked if she wore hearing aids. What the friend had in fact said was, 'My mother is dead.'

Occasionally the smile gives hearing people the impression that deaf people are not very quick-witted. Someone we know, who is married to a deaf person, calls this 'The deaf person's smile.'

Eve Nickerson, a cochlear implant user, recalls how her husband, Bill, who is a hearing person, described the problems that can arise for a hearing person, when their deaf partner does not admit that they have not heard something. 'Eve, when you don't understand [hear] what I'm saying, you get the oddest look on your face. I can't tell whether you're upset at me, wondering how to answer me, off in a fog, or just didn't understand what I said. It's confusing and upsetting for me. It must be for others too. You've got to tell us when you don't understand [hear]' (Thomsett and Nickerson, 1997).

Just because you're paranoid doesn't mean they're not out to get you!

Sometimes the world seems to be designed by hearing people for hearing people. This can be extremely frustrating and annoying and causes hard of hearing people to quite justifiably lose their tempers. Those who are not deaf sometimes find this mystifying. Let us give some examples taken from real life.

Your bank writes to you with a query and suggests that you telephone them at once to sort out the problem. The first cause of frustration is that you find using the telephone difficult or impossible. You might decide to write or send an email or fax instead. You might write and explain that, since you are deaf, you would appreciate an appointment to discuss the matter face to face with a real person. You might write an angry letter asking for a textphone number. You might ask a hearing friend or relative to telephone for you. Working out what to do is stressful and worrying. If your hearing friend had received a letter like this, they would simply have picked up the telephone.

However, suppose you decide to use your amplified telephone with its built-in loop system, what then? Well, you dial the number and a mechanical voice says, 'If you wish to rhubarb, rhubarb, rhubarb, press rhubarb. If you wish to blank, blank, blank, press blank.' And so on. You put the telephone down, take a deep breath and try again. You think you have to press 3. But you have to press 3 after the tone. You cannot hear the tone. You ask your partner for help. You hate having to do that because you like to be independent. Your partner makes the connection for you and hands you the receiver. A voice says, 'Please hold the line. You are in a queue.' Then some horrible music plays, which sets your tinnitus off. After ten minutes, someone answers the telephone. You realise with a sinking heart that they have a strong regional accent, which you are not used to, and you find them hard to understand. Is it any wonder that you might be a little terse with them and not so polite as you usually are?

Or imagine you have studied for years to obtain a qualification and now you are applying for a job. Then you come to something like this:

Do you have a disability that would make it unsafe for you at work?   *YES/NO*

How do you answer that?

◆   Yes, I have a disability but I'm not unsafe.
◆   No, I don't have a disability; I'm only deaf.
◆   Yes, I have a disability, but I'm not unsafe unless you ask me stupid questions like this one.

If you think we are exaggerating, we have actually read this on an application form. In what way do they think that anyone with a disability is more unsafe than anyone else?

Sick or sorry?

For the last example on this subject, let us look at our experiences in a hospital setting. If you had to sum up what a hospital is, how would you do it? Many people would say:

◆   A hospital is a place where sick people go to be cured.
◆   A hospital is a place where very ill people go to die.
◆   A hospital is a place where you go to have an operation.

How do deaf and hard of hearing people fit into that? They are not ill but deaf. For most deaf people there is no cure, no operation and no medical treatment. Once they have been examined, diagnosed and a few offered an operation or treatment if possible, the doctors have finished with them.

What deaf people are offered are things to help them live with deafness such as hearing aids, cochlear implants, lipreading classes, special equipment and so on. Yet, hospitals, for sick people, are where they are regularly sent.

Us and them

Hospitals are divided into we (deaf people) who are considered sick, and they (hearing professionals) who are not.

What can often happen in a hospital is that deaf people feel in an 'us' and 'them' situation. They, the medical profession, are the experts and have all the answers. They are 'superior' to us because of their knowledge and training and because they themselves are not ill or disabled. We are 'inferior' because we do not know what they know and we are the ones with the problem. Actually, deaf people are the experts! A person with a hearing loss knows exactly what they can and cannot hear. They know if their hearing aid hurts and exactly where it hurts. They know whether their hearing aid is working or not. They know where their tinnitus is and what it sounds like and how loud it is.

One woman with unpleasant tinnitus was asked which ear it was in.

'*Oh, it isn't in my ear, it's in my head.*'

'*You can't have tinnitus in your head*', said the expert.

(Actually, you can.) The woman was justifiably indignant. She was the one with the tinnitus and so she should have known where it was!

> 'Have you ever been told 'You should be able to hear that', or 'There's nothing wrong with the hearing aid' when you know that you cannot hear and the aid is making strange noises from time to time. A Hearing Therapist was once asked to visit a university campus to check the loop system in one of their lecture theatres. She was told that the deaf students had been complaining that the loop system was broadcasting pop music and they could not hear the lecturer speak. The member of staff who looked after the technical support system was adamant that this was impossible. The Hearing Therapist, who was deaf herself, switched her hearing aids on to 'T'. Sure enough, pop music. She told the staff member so and he refused to believe her. Wordlessly she took out one of her hearing aids and held it up to his ear. His face, when he heard the pop music loud and clear, was a sight to remember! It is always rash to say something is impossible! Much safer to say it is improbable or unlikely.

Why do deaf people become irritated? Not because they have less self-control than people with good hearing, nor because they 'have a chip on their shoulder' but because their lives are filled with situations like the above. Actually, it is amazing how good tempered and patient hard of hearing people are. The only wonder is that they do not lose their tempers more often!

Irritating things about being deaf

- ◆ Music does not sound the same through hearing aids.
- ◆ Some people think you are stupid. (It's mutual.)
- ◆ Conversation in groups and background noise is difficult.
- ◆ Romantic candlelit dinners mean you cannot hear so well because you cannot lipread.
- ◆ Sweet nothings really are nothings!
- ◆ Hearing aids/implants are not pretty.
- ◆ It is so boring having to tell people over and over again to please speak up, slow down, look at me, etc.
- ◆ Some hearing people find deafness puzzling and irritating.

Good things about being deaf

- You cannot hear your partner snore.
- You are not disturbed by car alarms going off in the street for hours at night.
- You can take your hearing aids out and really concentrate on your favourite hobby.
- You can switch off boring conversations.
- You do not have to listen to politicians, sport, soap operas on the television when the rest of the family are glued to the screen. (You could always go out, of course, but removing your hearing aids is sometimes easier.) And conversely, you can watch your favourite programmes with the sound off and the subtitles on if the rest of the family don't want to join in.
- You can really enjoy what you see, touch, taste and smell without being distracted by what you hear.
- Sometimes, silence is really beautiful.
- You can retreat into your own privacy whenever you want to.
- You have something in common with Beethoven, Queen Alexandra, Harriet Martineau, Jack Ashley, Helen Keller and lots of other famous and interesting people.
- You are a really good listener – you have to be!
- You can learn to lipread.
- It's nice to be different.

Finally in the words of a deaf French poet:

But without changing white into black
And disguising pain under the name of pleasure
I would say that (to one who knows the
Difference between good and evil)
Being deaf isn't as bad as it appears.'[1]

Joachim Du Bellay, quoted in David Wright, 1969.[2]

[English translation by Philip Tait]

Remember: **Deaf people are not ill, stupid, slow or unfortunate – just different!**

A quiet world

1. If you are hard of hearing or deaf, what is living in a quiet world like for you?

For example:

- When they are told that I am deaf, complete strangers feel they have the right to ask me how I went deaf.
- It's lovely not being able to hear the traffic.
- People assume that my partner, who is hearing, is a saint to put up with me.
- I really enjoy surprising people when I read their body language correctly.

More:

A

B

C

2. If you are hearing, what would you miss if you lived in a quiet world?

For example:

◆   I would miss being able to join in conversations easily.

◆   I would miss music.

◆   I would hate being patronised.

◆   I would miss the sound of rain.

More:

A

B

C

Notes

1 *Mais sans changer la blanche a la noire couleur,*
   Et sous nom de plaisir deguiser la douleur,
   Je dirai qu'être sourd (a qui la différence
   Sait du bien et du mal) n'est mal qu'en apparence.

2 David Wright is a well-known English writer and poet. He is also deaf.

Chapter 4

Hearing loss and its relationship to bereavement

The usual sound of the bacon frying was missing!! Ah well, perhaps it was just an unusually difficult morning with his hearing. The car refused to start – that could not be correct, as it had only just been serviced. There was no sound coming from it. He tried revving the engine – there was still no sound, but there was smoke coming from the exhaust and the steering wheel was vibrating. Slowly it dawned on him that the ENT consultant's cautionary words were coming true: he had lost some more of his hearing. Sounds had been 'squashy' for some time, rather like unintelligible noise through a thin partition, and he had to strain to understand what people said. But now he was unable to hear the familiar everyday sounds that had become so much of his daily life. He could not hear the breakfast cooking or the sound of his car starting up. He had lost the remaining sounds that enabled him to feel part of the world. At first he could not believe it, then he was angry – why had this happened to him? He had followed all the suggestions about eating healthily and he had even stopped smoking. Perhaps he should have tried harder and he felt embarrassed about not coping better. He felt depressed about his future. He was already struggling to understand people in the wine club and colleagues in meetings.

If you have a loss of hearing that has occurred suddenly or developed slowly, the situation described above may be familiar to you, and you have possibly experienced feelings of loss. It is important to realise that this is perfectly normal and you will come through it. Your loss of hearing may have left you grieving for your life as it was before you began to miss parts of words; and before you felt less sure about how to respond to a remark because you felt quite doubtful about what you *thought you had heard*, and then when the other person looked at you oddly, you realised that you *had probably misheard* them.

On a personal level, you may have lost the ability to communicate and take pleasure in things that you previously took for granted, such as hearing a friend talk to you; the companionable feeling of taking part in a group discussion; easily chatting to people; listening to the radio, television and music and being part of the world around you. You may have lost the ability to do all these things and therefore experienced the feeling that you have lost the person you were. You have perhaps begun to realise that your personality is changing, and you have become accustomed to withdrawing from some situations that you know you will find difficult.

You may have lost a job or the possibility of furthering your career, and this may have affected your financial security and status. Compounded with this you may have found it difficult to access any educational opportunities available to you.

These are all major losses akin to divorce, death, a change in health or mobility. They affect people deeply and feelings of grief occur. This grief is not just a feeling of sadness – feelings of anger and disbelief are common and quite a normal reaction. Everyone has different ways of coping with pain and loss, and some people overcome these feelings quicker than others.

There are different ways that hearing loss develops. You may have lost yours gradually or it may have occurred finally and suddenly, and it may well be that your way of coping will depend on your circumstances, the level of support you receive and your attitude towards the change that has occurred.

Elizabeth Kubler-Ross in her groundbreaking book *On Death and Dying* describes the grieving process as a normal reaction to a loss of any kind and involves five stages. These stages should be viewed with caution as much depends on a person's lifestyle, support and background, and some people take more time to move from one to another.

◆ The first stage is denial – this hasn't really happened to me. You may not believe that your hearing has become less effective and refuse to believe that there is no cure.

◆ The second stage is anger towards everyone involved with you, and everyone connected with the loss, e.g. audiologists and doctors.

◆ The third stage is bargaining – if only my hearing comes back, I'll be nicer to my family. This reaction comes because perhaps you feel responsible for the hearing loss and perhaps feel guilty – if only I had not sat so near the loud music, etc.

◆ The fourth stage is depression when the reality of the lasting effects of a hearing loss become apparent, and you realise that the situation will not change and the future appears bleak.

◆ The final stage is acceptance and this will occur at different times for each individual. Any kind of loss will still make a person sad, sometimes for several years, but the painful feelings will subside with time, making room for good positive feelings such as hope and trust in the future.

A 67-year-old hard of hearing man was stuck in the stages of denial, anger and bargaining for several years. He finally accepted his hearing loss when he joined a lipreading class and shared his experience with others. He acknowledged he had been depressed, and moved through to acceptance and took responsibility for the changes that he needed to make in order to communicate better.

It is worth remembering that it is natural to feel anger and grief and it is healthy to express this, and to cry or to say what you feel. Sometimes we need to talk to someone and release all the feelings by doing this and get in touch with the uncomfortable. A close friend, or someone with whom you feel comfortable, can be invaluable at this difficult time in helping you come to terms with your loss. This may lessen the period of depression, which is normal. You may experience a loss of confidence in yourself; feel very defensive, inadequate and stupid, a nuisance or have a low self-worth. These negative feelings can result in you developing an antisocial attitude and alienate you further from family and friends, who will not always understand your distressing situation.

The experience of a hearing loss, be it gradual or sudden, inevitably means a major change in communication. Situations that were previously taken for granted cause an immense amount of stress. The sheer emotional strain of trying to cope in social situations, where you cannot understand what is happening, result in frustration, poor concentration, fatigue, feelings of anxiety, confusion and embarrassment.

There is not always an easy way to deal with the overwhelming feeling of loss that you may experience when you lose some or all of your hearing. The founder of the American organisation, Self Help for Hard of Hearing People (SHHH), Howard E 'Rocky' Stone, recognised the deep distress caused by a loss of hearing. He acquired a hearing loss in his late teens. In later years, when he became blind, he received a cochlear implant. He died in 2004 after many years of working tirelessly, in many capacities, for deaf and hard of hearing people. In his book *An Invisible Condition* he wrote a chapter entitled 'Become healers … and heal yourselves'. He acknowledged that turning inwards, self pity, withdrawal and bitter feelings were the result of the pain of loss. He recommended that instead of being diminished by the experience of pain, it could be used as a healer and viewed as 'a gift of the wounded'. He observed that when pain is experienced, it may well be used to alleviate pain in others. He viewed it as being a channel for changing priorities and focusing on more meaningful things and becoming more aware of each other. He considered this was a precondition for 'healing'.

Organisations for deaf and hard of hearing people have many volunteers who are using their experience to 'heal' that of others, to encourage and support people who could once hear and who feel devastated by a real loss of sense of identity.

We have compiled some suggestions, which we are hopeful will support you as you journey along the challenging road towards acceptance.

1. **Take time out when you feel under pressure because of the loss of concentration and stress you may be experiencing.** You could perhaps leave the room for a while, do some breathing exercises and consciously relax.
2. **Give yourself some space and affirm to yourself that you have a lot to contribute.** If you have the emotional energy, return to the situation and say that you are not able to understand all the conversation and ask the people to let you know what you have been missing or make some similar request. This assertive activity will depend on what feels comfortable for you.
3. **Constantly affirm to yourself that you are important**, that you are worth the fuss and have a right to ask for people's co-operation.
4. **Try to keep a sense of humour and a light touch.**
5. **Relaxation, yoga, a good diet, exercise and sleep all help.**
6. **Enjoy a good hobby or entertainment.**
7. **Work at changing your attitude by mentally practising positive thoughts about seemingly impossible situations.** For example, being invited to a wedding and knowing that you will have to sit at a table with people whom you do not know may fill you with dread. You are worried the light will be poor or there will be too much background noise. Focus on recognising why you are feeling annoyed. Is it realistic to use up so much emotional energy on being upset, when, perhaps, if you apply experience and logic to the reasons you are feeling the way you are, there is actually no evidence to back up your concerns? Acknowledge that perhaps you are feeling vulnerable because of previous negative experiences and that you learnt from the situation, and will now prepare yourself positively for a challenging situation by asking to sit in the most favourable position for you to lipread people at the table, and taking a pen and paper for further support.
8. **Develop awareness of the world beyond yourself by learning to let go of resentment, fear and negative thinking.**
9. **Meditation, prayer and faith can help some people.**
10. **Trust in something outside yourself, accept your limitations and acknowledge all that is good and positive in yourself and in other people.**
11. **You may find some healing in silence and develop an inner life which is rich and fulfilling.**

12. **Perhaps you will develop an increased appreciation of nature, literature and art.**

13. **An increased development of intuition and perception may compensate for not hearing**, and you may develop less dependence on this sense for awareness and communication. Perhaps you may find that you have developed a knack for identifying what colours work well together and how much space is required for a certain piece of furniture in a room. You may also be able to interpret the meaning of gestures that people use so that they provide you with clues for understanding speech better, because you are not so distracted by sound and have become more observant.

14. **Finally give yourself permission to grieve in a manner that you may not be intellectually comfortable with, but which you find emotionally satisfying.**

Chapter 5

Realistic expectations

Whether we have a disability or not, all of us eventually have to come to terms with realistic expectations. What do we mean by that? It means the realisation that we have limits; that, much as we would like, there are things that we are not going to achieve or to obtain. We are not all going to be millionaires by the time we are thirty; we are not all going to be great writers; we are not all going to have four perfect children each; we are not all going to be famous. It is at the point that we realise what we cannot do that we begin to understand what we can do and aim for that instead. Life is a strange combination of knowing our limitations and yet still aiming high.

Having unrealistic expectations when one has a hearing loss can make for a great deal of unhappiness. What sort of unrealistic expectations do people with a hearing loss often have?

'There is a miracle cure for deafness'

Deafness is caused by a variety of things and finding a cure depends on what has caused your deafness. For example, if your deafness has been caused by a blockage of wax in your ear, then it is usually curable. The doctor will prescribe some drops to soften the wax so that it can be removed by syringing or suction. End of problem. If the deafness has been caused by an infection, then it is probably curable depending on how bad the infection is and how long it has gone on for. Again, the doctor may prescribe drops or antibiotics to clear up the infection and may clean the ear out. Once the infection has gone you should be able to hear better – unless the infection has left permanent damage to the ear.[1] If deafness has been caused by a perforation of the eardrum or damage to the little bones (the ossicles) in the ear, there are operations that can sometimes put the damage right. However, if the deafness is caused by changes in the cochlea or damage to the auditory nerve, then there is little hope of recovery. Even a cochlear implant is merely a kind of hearing aid fitted inside the head instead of outside. Hearing loss is usually permanent; there is no miracle cure although some things may help.

'Hearing aids give you perfect hearing'

A hearing aid is merely something that helps you to hear better. It cannot give you your hearing back. A hard of hearing or deaf person wearing a hearing aid is still deaf. If you are issued with a hearing aid, whether analogue or digital, NHS or private, in-the-ear or behind-the-ear, visible or invisible – it makes no difference, you will still not hear perfectly. Pay what you like, go where you like, see as many experts as you like – it is just the same. Hearing aids are to ears what a walking stick is to a person with severe arthritis. A walking stick helps a person with arthritis to get around more easily. It does not cure their arthritis. A hearing aid will help you hear better; you will not hear perfectly.

A patient will sometimes expect their hearing aid to do what even a perfectly functioning ear cannot do! All audiology departments have a story about the person who walks in and says something like, 'My hearing aid is no use to me because when I am watching television in the lounge and my wife is vacuuming the carpet in the hall with the door shut, I cannot hear what she is saying!'

Perhaps some of you will remember Sam Weller in Charles Dickens' novel *The Pickwick Papers* being asked in a court of law why he had not seen something take place: 'Yes, I have a pair of eyes', replied Sam, 'and that's just it. If they was a pair of patent double million magnifying gas microscopes of extra power, perhaps I might be able to see through a flight of stairs and a deal door; but being only eyes, you see, my vision's limited.'[2]

Sam could not see up a flight of stairs and through a closed wooden door because he had only normal eyes and not bionic ones! Hearing aids cannot enable a hard of hearing person to hear things that are impossible even for someone with unimpaired hearing to hear!

Some people assume that there is a perfect hearing aid somewhere that will give them everything that they want, or even that the NHS has such hearing aids but refuses to give them to its patients. Be logical – if such a miracle hearing aid existed, don't you think you would be given it right away? Are NHS staff trained to be deliberately cruel or thoughtless? Surely the bottom line is that they would give you whatever would make you happy, if only to stop you coming back week after week!

A hearing aid will help you hear some things, but it will not help you hear everything. We mean no disrespect to hearing aid manufacturers – but no piece of technology, however excellent, is any substitute for the real thing. The only perfect hearing aid is a human ear!

'Lipreading and communication tactics are for people who are completely deaf'

If you go to your GP with headaches and he recommends that you see an optician about getting some glasses, you do not object that they are no use to you because you're only a little short-sighted. On the contrary, you are delighted to have found something that will get rid of those headaches and prevent eyestrain, even if you are surprised to discover that you are short-sighted. In the same way, if you visit your doctor because you are having problems hearing and he sends you to a specialist who recommends a hearing aid and lipreading, do not reject lipreading on the basis that you are only 'a little hard of hearing'. Hearing aids are one thing that can help you, lipreading is a second thing, and communication tactics are a third. If you add them all together you will derive more benefit than from just using hearing aids on their own.

'Technology can do anything'

Yes, well it would be comforting to think so! Special equipment to help people with a disability is useful to help compensate for that disability – it cannot perform miracles. People with a hearing loss sometimes need help to be alerted to the doorbell so a flashing light doorbell or a portable one may be suggested.

Objections to special equipment are sometimes made by hard of hearing people, for example you cannot always be looking at the flashing light, or you might forget to carry the portable one around with you. The objections mean that the technology is limited. All technology is limited, even for a hearing person! Even if you have perfect hearing you have to be within earshot of your ordinary doorbell – your being at the bottom of the garden or in the bath limits the usefulness of the technology whether you are hearing or deaf. That's life!

'People are automatically nice to you because you have a disability'

Being hard of hearing, having a disability, being in poor health, being old, being unemployed, do not automatically qualify us for special consideration, unfortunately.

One of the reasons for this is that all these things are invisible and people do not realise you have a problem because they cannot see it. The good news is that most people are nice once you have told them what your problem is. When you have told the lady in the bank that you cannot hear, she will usually smile, slow down her speech, face you, repeat what she has said and write things down. However, this is not always the case and is something that we just have to accept. Perhaps the person you are talking to has worse problems of their own. Examples that often occur are people who are worried about someone they love who is ill; someone who has just suffered a bereavement; someone who has just been told that they have a serious illness; someone who is in pain; someone who has just lost their job. Other people have their own problems too and they might be worse than yours. The world is full of pleasant people, but occasionally you will meet some of the other sort!

Always remember that it is not your fault that you are deaf. If someone is rude to you merely because of your hearing loss, they have the problem – not you!

'Everything that goes wrong in my life is a result of my hearing loss'

Be fair, some things are the result of your hearing loss, but not everything. Perhaps you did not do well at school because you could not hear the lessons properly, but perhaps you did not do as much studying as you might have done. Perhaps your neighbour ignores you because you are deaf, but perhaps he is shy and would love you to speak to him first. Perhaps your job is boring, but is it really impossible to change it? More things are affected by having a hearing loss than people with good hearing realise – but not everything is worse as a result. Some things are better! People who are hard of hearing or deaf are not woken in the night by thunderstorms, car alarms or traffic. They can switch off unpleasant noises during the day by turning their hearing aids down or off. They are able to concentrate when reading or studying because they are not distracted by background sounds. It is possible to sit on a busy train and enjoy one's book completely oblivious to those around who are chatting, using their mobile telephones and generally being noisy.

'Having a hearing loss means giving up things you enjoy'

It is true that having a hearing loss makes a difference to one's life. Sometimes it means giving up a hobby or a leisure pursuit that one enjoys but think very carefully before you do this. Is it really necessary or is there a way around the problem? Do you have to give up going to bingo or could you transfer to the new bingo hall, which has a loop system? Do you have to give up your committee work, or would a loop system, Palantypist or lip-speaker solve the problem? Do you have to give up singing in the choir? Several professional musicians wear hearing aids and are still able to continue in their work.

If you have to let something go, is it possible to put something equally enjoyable in its place? If you give up going to concerts, can you go to art galleries instead? If you have to give up chatting on the telephone, can you learn to use email? If you have to give up going to your local pub because it is too noisy, how about inviting a few friends round for a social evening in your home instead? Suit your lifestyle and your leisure to your hearing – it will be less frustrating and more enjoyable.

> I am aware of Sylvana recounting animated stories to Nicole about her father. Right now she's telling her how difficult it has become to accompany the old man to the theatre. The principle [sic] problem, apart from the fact that he's confined to crutches and has crap eyesight, is that he's totally deaf.

Nicole is nodding gravely, a portrait of total concern. She appears to be deeply affected by the fact that Sylvana's father is thus misfortuned.

'So what he does is this,' my friend continues, encouraged. 'He buys the play first and reads it, commits it to memory and follows it on the night from the actors' lips.'

Nicole is now shaking her head in awe, chanting what a wonderful achievement this is for Sylvana's father at his age, adding at the last minute that age shouldn't matter at all.

Brian Gallagher, *The Feng-Shui Junkie*

It is helpful in this respect to think of deafness as part of the ageing process, which it is for many people. With age, all of us have to give up some of the things we have enjoyed over the years. The 60-year-old does not behave like the 16-year-old. Age causes the professional athlete to coach rather than run; the ballet dancer to teach instead of dance; the successful businessman to retire. Look on deafness as an opportunity to embrace change as well as losing something you value.

Having said all this, do not let other people decide for you. People with disabilities are often told, by people without disabilities, 'You cannot do ...' You might agree with them, but you do not have to. We know of someone who, when diagnosed with epilepsy when aged 14, was told, 'You will never be able to learn to drive, go to college, have a career, marry, or have children.' She saw this as a challenge and has since done all these things. Limitation or challenge? Your choice.

'I could not possibly ask people to look at me when they speak'

Be reasonable and expect other people to be reasonable too. It is realistic to expect other people, once you have told them you have a hearing loss, to:

◆ look at you when they speak to you
◆ to speak clearly and just a little slower
◆ to repeat things, rephrasing if necessary
◆ to write something down if you cannot understand them.

It is not reasonable to expect them to do these things if you refuse to wear your hearing aid, do not look at the person talking to you, or stop concentrating!

It is realistic to expect the NHS to provide:

◆ the best hearing aids that they can afford
◆ an accessible repair service
◆ rehabilitation, counselling, advice and information
◆ a polite and courteous service.

'Who is to blame?'

Finally, blame the right people. Complaining to the receptionist in your local Audiology Department about the length of time you have had to wait for your digital hearing aid may make you feel better, but it will not help change the system. (It will not help the poor receptionist either, who gets shouted at several times a day.) You may have to wait because the department is short of staff. There may be twenty thousand hearing aid patients living in your area and only three audiologists working at your local hospital. The receptionist can do nothing to change this. The audiologist can do nothing to change this. Complain to the people at the top who decide funding and staffing levels.

Write to the Chief Executive of your local hospital. Complain to your MP. This is why organisations like the Royal National Institute for Deaf People (RNID) lead national campaigns!

The answer to unrealistic expectations is – be reasonable! Life is so much easier when you are.

Things to think about

This section is for you to fill in. Tick or ring your answers or fill in your thoughts on the lines. Be as honest as you can. If you do not want other people to read your thoughts, photocopy the pages and fill in the photocopies.

1. What should I like to be able to hear that I cannot hear?
e.g. hear birdsong

_____

Is this realistic?   **YES/NO**

YES, if I wear my hearing aid.
Are you wearing your hearing aid when you go outside?

_____

NO, because I have a high frequency hearing loss.

2. What should I like to be able to do?
e.g. use a telephone

_____

Is this possible?   **YES/NO**

If **YES**, what steps am I taking to make this possible (e.g. buying an amplified telephone)?

_____

If **NO**, what could I do instead (e.g. learn to use email or text messaging on a mobile phone)?

_____

3. How has my hearing loss changed my life?
Negative things, e.g. I cannot hear music as well as I could

a. _____

b. _____

c. _____

Positive things, e.g. I have learned to use a computer

a. _____

b. _____

c. _____

4. What have I had to give up because of my hearing loss?
e.g. singing in the choir

a. _____

b. _____

c. _____

5. What new experiences have I had because of my hearing loss?
e.g. going on a Hearing Concern holiday with other deaf people

a. _____

b. _____

c. _____

6. What should I like to change about my life?
e.g. I feel very isolated

a. _____

b. _____

c. _____

7. How could I change things?
e.g. I could find a penfriend

a. _____

b. _____

c. _____

8. During the next year, what should I like to achieve for myself?
e.g. learn to swim

a. _____

b. _____

c. _____

9. What should I like to achieve for others?
e.g. raise some money for my favourite charity

a. _____

b. _____

c. _____

10. Something I have always wanted to do.
e.g. travel

_____

How could I do this?
e.g. start saving, find a friend to go with, etc.

_____

Off you go!

Notes
1 Ear infections should not be neglected. If left untreated, ear infections can lead to permanent ear damage, such as scarring of the eardrum and subsequent partial loss of hearing. Always see your GP if you think you may have an ear infection.
2 I have translated Sam's reply out of Cockney to aid clarity.

Chapter 6

Assertiveness

Do you find your biggest problem is communicating with hearing people whom you do not know, and asking them for help, or telling people that you are deaf or hard of hearing?

This chapter is about how to ask for the changes you require in order to understand speech better without sounding rude or aggressive, and how to let others know that you are having a problem. It is about being assertive, which basically means the ability to express your thoughts and feelings in a way that clearly states your needs, and keeps the lines of communication open with the other person.

However, first a basic assumption has to be made. You will be taking the main responsibility for ensuring that you are able to comprehend what is said to you. You must do as much as you can to help yourself. If you are unwilling to do this, or are unable to do so for some reason, then you cannot reasonably expect others to do it for you. If you are asking for help, you should not be apologetic, as if you are doing something to feel guilty about. A loss of hearing can happen to anyone.

Being assertive is about having needs and expressing them. You must believe you have an entitlement to the following rights:

- The right to state your own needs and set your own priorities independent of any roles you may assume in your life. This includes pursuing your own goals and dreams and establishing your own priorities.
- The right to be treated with respect for your own values, beliefs, opinions and emotions as an intelligent and capable human being, no matter what the opinion of others may be.
- The right not to have to justify or explain your actions or feelings to others.
- The right to express yourself, and to say 'No', 'I don't know', and 'I don't understand'. You have the right to take the time you need to formulate your ideas before expressing them.
- The right to ask for information or help without having negative feelings about your needs.
- The right to change your mind, to make mistakes, and to sometimes act illogically – with full understanding and acceptance of the consequences.
- The right to like yourself, even though you're not perfect, and to sometimes do less than you are capable of doing.
- The right to have positive, satisfying relationships within which you feel comfortable and free to express yourself honestly – and the right to change or end relationships if they don't meet your needs.
- The right to change, enhance or develop your life in any way you determine and not be dependent on others for approval.
- The right to tell others how you wish to be treated and say yes and no for yourself.

Assertiveness strategies

Telling people you are deaf
- I've got a slight hearing loss and need to lipread.

- I don't hear as well as I used to.
- I wear a hearing aid and I need to lipread.
- With all this noise I can't hear that well.
- I'm a bit deaf/hard of hearing.
- I am deaf and I am lipreading you.

Asking for help – what would you say (in your own words)

- Speak a little louder, but don't shout?
- Face me when you speak, because I need to lipread?
- Speak a little slower?
- Move away from that noise with me?
- Turn down the television?
- Remove that pipe/cigarette when you speak to me?
- Move away from that window?
- Tell me when you change topics?
- Speak as clearly as possible?
- Rephrase what you said?
- Speak one person at a time?
- Spell, or write down, that word?
- Keep your hand away from your mouth?
- Sit with me away from the noise?
- Repeat the last word/sentence/the person's name?

> Remember to tell the speaker when they have been helpful to you. If the speaker later forgets, remember that old habits are hard to change. If the speaker seems impatient when reminded, try to remember that both listener and speaker could be experiencing tiredness. The listener must try to have as much patience with the speaker as they would like from the speaker.

Would you do any of the following?

- Use your hearing aids all the time?
- Use assistive listening devices?
- Change things around you?
- Arrange your seating so that you can see the speaker's face?
- Arrange seating so you are close to others?
- Position yourself so you are in the best position for talking with someone else?
- Arrive early so you can choose the best seat for you?
- Wear your glasses if you need them for lipreading?
- Keep a pen and pad handy so people can write down a difficult word you haven't been able to lipread?
- Keep informed on likely topics of conversation?
- Be honest about not hearing and acknowledge fatigue and postpone an interaction until you are rested?
- Inform others how they can help?

Examples of assertive behaviour

1. **Francesco and Annabel are keen members of their local church. Francesco suddenly loses his hearing as the result of a viral infection. He is no longer able to understand the priest, and he becomes very angry and upset.**

   Passive solution: Not to go to the church anymore.
   Aggressive solution: Become angry with the priest because he should know how to speak clearly.
   Assertive solution:
   ◆ Ask to the see the priest and explain his needs.
   ◆ Move down to the front of the church.
   ◆ Ask for a copy of the sermon before the service.
   ◆ When it feels comfortable, let other congregants know what they can do to help.

2. **Henrietta and Irene have been attending the theatre together for many years. Irene's hearing deteriorates as the result of presbyacusis and she has to use two hearing aids. She complains that she thinks the actors are not speaking as clearly as they used to.**

   Passive solution: To stay at home and watch the television.
   Aggressive solution: Blame the hearing aids and stop using them.
   Assertive solution:
   ◆ Visit the audiologist to have the hearing aids checked to ensure they are not faulty.
   ◆ Read a synopsis of the play before attending the theatre.
   ◆ Make enquiries about the availability of assistive listening devices in the theatre.
   ◆ Tell Henrietta about the change in her hearing and advise her how she can help.

3. **Bob has had a partial hearing loss all his life. He frequently becomes angry when he is using public transport because he is unsure what is happening when all the passengers get off before the end of the journey.**

   Passive solution: Follow other passengers or abandon the journey and become increasingly anxious and annoyed.
   Aggressive solution: Blame the transport system for not putting up visual messaging. Stop using public transport.
   Assertive solution:
   ◆ Advise another passenger that he has a hearing loss and has to lipread, and ask if he can tell him what is happening.
   ◆ Carry pen and paper for exact information.
   ◆ Seek out an official and explain his situation.
   ◆ Prepare himself for this occurrence by carrying a card saying he has a loss of hearing and what he needs for them to communicate more easily.
   ◆ Wear a badge under his lapel denoting he has a hearing loss, which he can put on view if he is unable to understand what a person is saying.

Chapter 7

Lipreading

This chapter is about lipreading or, as it has also been known, dental audition, labial augury, labiomancy, labiology, lip reading, ocular audition, oral audition, speech-reading, visual hearing, visual listening and visual communication. Over the years, lipreading has been referred to by all of these titles. Since the art of lipreading involves many different skills, academics and researchers tend to refer to lipreading as speechreading. However, most people who use it regularly and those who teach it in this country refer to it as lipreading. That is the term we shall use in this chapter.

Before the advent of hearing aids, people who lost their hearing as adults had no choice but to learn to lipread. As early as 1648 a man called John Bulwer was referring to lipreading as: '... that subtle art which may enable one with an observant eye to hear what any man speaks by the moving of his lips' (John Bulwer, *Philocophus, or, The Deaf and Dumb Man's Friend*).[1]

What are the skills involved in lipreading?

Lipreading does not just mean watching the speaker's lips. It may involve any or all of the following:

- watching the movements of the speaker's mouth, teeth and tongue;
- reading the expression on the speaker's face;
- noticing the speaker's body language and gestures;
- using your own residual hearing;
- anticipation.

A nice summary of lipreading is found in the following quotation: '[Lipreading is] the ability to understand a speaker's thoughts by watching the movements of the face and body and by using information provided by the situation and the language' (Kaplan, Bally, Scott and Garretson, 1995).

Who uses lipreading?

Nearly everyone! Research has shown that even hearing people hear better when they can see the face of the person who is talking to them (especially in noisy situations). 'In people who can hear and see perfectly well there were further intriguing studies – seeing the speaker's mouth aids comprehension even with good auditory input.' (Campbell, Dodd and Burnham, 1998).

Lipreading is used by many people who have a hearing loss. Of the eight million people in Britain who have a hearing loss, 70,000 use British Sign Language as their preferred method of communication. Nearly everyone else will rely to some extent on lipreading.

When someone loses their hearing, they are very commonly asked why they do not learn Sign Language. Well, why don't they? There are two main reasons. Most people who lose their hearing are adults over the age of 60. Their preferred language is speech. British Sign Language (BSL) is a complex and beautiful language in its own right. It has its own grammar and extensive vocabulary. To learn it well enough to become fluent in it would take years. The second reason is this. Imagine you are a retired insurance salesman of 62. You have noticed a steady decrease in your hearing over the last few years. You have just been given your first hearing aid. It is helpful, but not completely so. A friend suggests you learn BSL to help communication and to prevent you from becoming isolated. You go to evening classes to learn. You are enthusiastic and after five years of hard work, you become reasonably fluent. While talking to your friend one day, you experience problems in hearing his replies. You switch to using BSL. Now he does not understand you. He has not learned Sign Language. Neither has your wife, or the man in the corner shop, or your grandson. The advantage of lipreading is that most people use speech to communicate.

Sympathetic and imaginative hearing people often comment that it must be dreadful to lose one's hearing and be unable to hear the birds sing or to hear music clearly. People who are musicians or twitchers (bird watchers) who become hard of hearing might agree with that, but most people who lose their hearing as adults would say that the thing they miss most is ease of communication with others. They miss being able to relax and chat, especially in a group of people. They may be able to hold their own in a conversation, despite being deaf, but from now on it is an effort and a strain.

> The deafness which alienates and dehumanises us is caused by inaccessible words. To be denied access to language which takes liberties with you is an assault on your control over your life. The human contact deaf people need is what causes us the greatest unhappiness.
> Diane Kenyon, 'Reaction–Interaction', in Keith (ed.) *Mustn't Grumble*

Lipreading aims to lessen the effort and reduce the strain. Lipreading is about training your eyes to help your ears. 'Even to a greater degree can the deaf man train his eye to substitute for his deaf ears' (Nitchie, 2004).[2]

How can anyone learn to lipread?

The good news, as we have already discovered, is that we all can all lipread to a certain extent already. This means that you are not so much learning to lipread as improving an ability you already have. People who lose their hearing often gradually find that their lipreading skills have imperceptibly improved without them realising it. Some people think that they can still hear quite well until the person speaking to them turns away. It is only then that the hard of hearing person realises that they have been lipreading all along!

Some people buy or borrow a book about lipreading and learn using a mirror or with the help of a family member or friend (see Appendix 2, Further Reading). There are lipreading videos and CD-ROMs available.[3] Many people enjoy joining a local lipreading class. It is the responsibility of the local Adult Education Service to provide these so ask at your local college. Some local Audiology Departments run their own lipreading classes. The Association of Teachers of Lipreading to Adults will be able to tell you if there is a lipreading class near you (see Appendix 1 for address). If there is not, why not campaign to get one started? Remember how many people would find lipreading helpful!

So what's a lipreading class like?

A lipreading class is full of people like you! It is full of people who have lost their hearing as adults. Apart from that, you may find you are all widely different from each other. Hearing loss is no respecter of persons. You may find an accountant in her thirties, a retired teacher, a factory worker in his fifties, a police marksman, a granny who sings in the local choir, a professional musician in her forties and so on.

People in lipreading classes come in all shapes and sizes and ages, although for obvious reasons many will be above retirement age. They come from both sexes and from all social and ethnic groups. There is no age limit; classes regularly have people of over 90 who learn to lipread successfully. No qualifications are needed. The university professor may find it more difficult to learn to lipread than the housewife.

You will find that having a hearing loss unites you and makes you friends in a special way. Being part of a lipreading class does not just mean that you learn lipreading; you will also find the help and support of those who have similar problems to your own. When you chat at the tea-break of the difficulties you experience when shopping, they will tell you that they have the same trouble, but they will also tell you how they manage and what they do to cope.

Each session usually lasts for about two hours with a tea or coffee break in the middle. Why do you take a break?

◆ Lipreading is tiring and you will need an 'eye-break' to refresh yourself and maintain your concentration.
◆ Your teacher may also be deaf! Many lipreading teachers are. He/she will need a break just as you do.
◆ Taking a break enables you to practise listening in background noise as you enjoy a cup of tea and a chat with your classmates.
◆ You can exchange tips with each other in an informal setting on how to cope with hearing loss and this can be very helpful.

Each week the class concentrates on a particular lipreading shape, for example the shape that looks like 'p'. The teacher will show you the shape and explain which shapes look similar to it and which look very different. 'P' looks like 'b' and 'm' but very different from 'v' or 'sh'. (Have a look in the mirror.) She will then show you the shape over and over again in different ways, but without using her voice. By the end of the lesson, you will recognise the shape much more easily. (See the exercises at the end of this chapter.)

You begin by learning to recognise shapes with your conscious mind. This is a slow process. Eventually, you can recognise shapes without thinking about them consciously and do it at high speed. You will find that you can do several things at once:

◆ Lipread some of the shapes (consonant shapes are usually easier to lipread than vowel shapes).
◆ Hear some of the sounds (vowel shapes are usually easier to hear than consonant shapes).
◆ Recognise and interpret facial expression, body language and gesture.
◆ 'Put two and two together' and guess words that you can neither lipread or hear by using the context and common sense to help you.
◆ Put them all together at top speed and respond appropriately!

Strangely enough, sentences are easier to lipread than individual words and long words are easier to lipread than short words. This always impresses hearing people! *Would you like a cup of tea?* is easier to lipread than *Tea?* and *Buttercup* is easier to lipread than *But*.

Despite having a serious purpose, the lesson is meant to be light-hearted and fun. Class members often say that they have enjoyed the lesson so much, they have forgotten they were learning to lipread!

Here are some of the things that you can also learn while lipreading.

Confidence

People who lose their hearing can also lose their confidence. If you are not sure what people are saying you might take less part in conversation, hesitate to use the telephone and prefer not to chat to people when you are out. Sometimes, people withdraw from their family and friends altogether. This is a great shame and can result in the person becoming very lonely. Learning to lipread often gives people their confidence back. Why? Well, you learn that your 'mistakes', which you thought were due to your hearing loss, were in fact lipreading confusions owing to the fact that some words look very similar to others on the lips. Your so-called errors were, in fact, reasonable, sensible and intelligent. For example:

> **Hearing friend**: I only paid fifteen pounds for that.
> **Hard of hearing listener**: Wasn't fifty pounds rather expensive?

The confusion has arisen because the words *fifteen* and *fifty* look the same to the lipreader. (Look in the mirror and compare them.) If your friend is usually extravagant, the error is even more likely to arise!

Some people imagine that, because the sense of hearing is less acute, the brain has been affected also! Not so. One of the lipreading class members remarked that he was going to have a T-shirt made with the slogan on it: I'M DEAF NOT DAFT!

Social skills

Occasionally a hard of hearing person will have become so withdrawn from the world around them that they have almost forgotten how to chat socially. Lipreading classes involve practising lipreading useful everyday phrases such as:

> *'Cold enough for you?'*
> *'Tea or coffee?'*
> *'Would you like cashback?'*
> *'Have you had your holiday yet?'*

Some lipreading teachers organise class outings to interesting places and arrange for a lipspeaker to be present if a talk or lecture is given.

Communication tactics and repair strategies, or, how to cheat!

When you learn communication tactics, you are learning how to use your environment to help you. It is easier to hear when you are facing the person talking to you; when the television is turned off; when the light is switched on. You can learn to feel the draught from the door opening rather than hear the sound. You can feel the vibration of the underground train approaching and the air from the tunnel rather than hear it coming. You can see someone approaching from their reflection in the shop window rather than hear their footsteps.

You will also learn repair strategies. What do you do when you have not heard and you cannot lipread? Well, you could ask a closed question, e.g. 'Did you say fifteen minutes?' You could ask the other person to write the information down. You could relax and decide not to bother and concentrate on the next part of the conversation! You can apologise, put the telephone down and write a letter instead.

No-one ever said that it was compulsory to hear everything!

Change your life

Going to a lipreading class can not only be life-enhancing but also life-changing. You may learn how to retrain and change your career. People who are in jobs where they are struggling to hear may decide to access the training and grants on offer and take the opportunity to move off in an entirely new direction. We have known people change from being unemployed to being a computer programmer; from being an insurance clerk to being a gardener; and from being a teacher to being a Hearing Therapist. A class member who heard during a class about the charity Hearing Dogs for Deaf People decided to apply for a Hearing Dog. She did so and acquired one, with the result that her life was totally transformed. So, beware, going to lipreading classes can be exciting and challenging! It can totally change your life.

What makes a good lipreader?

Research has shown some encouraging, but unsurprising facts:

- Deaf people are better lipreaders than hearing people.
- People with a good deal of experience of hearing speech are better lipreaders than those who have less experience.
- People whose first language is speech lipread well.
- People who read a lot make good lipreaders.

What else can help?

- A good memory. Some lipreading teachers organise memory-training exercises such as Kim's Game.[4]
- General knowledge. Reading the daily paper or watching the news.
- Liking words. Crosswords, word puzzles and Scrabble can be fun and can help here.
- Being willing to 'have a go'. Who cares what other people think? We are all in this together. If you make a mistake you can learn from it – and so can the other class members. In any case, who will remember tomorrow that you did not get it right today?

What are the advantages and disadvantages of lipreading?

Be reasonable about lipreading. It is not possible to lipread every word, but it is possible to lipread many of the words and to understand the sense of what people are saying so that you can take an intelligent part in a conversation. Lipreading takes longer to learn than one or two lessons.

> A lipreading student-teacher was observing a local lipreading class. The class members were all enthusiastic about lipreading and spoke movingly of how helpful it was – except for one man. This particular class member was complaining bitterly about the uselessness of lipreading. The student asked him how long he had been trying to learn. 'Two whole lessons!' he replied indignantly.[5]

When you have mastered lipreading you will not be able to lipread Serbo-Croat at one-hundred yards. Unfortunately, this is an idea that one often finds in the media or in detective novels. Hearing people often think that if you can lipread, you can lipread anything, however unlikely.[6]

Certain situations are easier to lipread in than others. When Dr Johnson visited a school for deaf children in Scotland in the eighteenth century he was impressed with their lipreading abilities but he noticed that the person speaking to the children had to look at them and speak reasonably clearly: 'if he that speaks looks towards them [the deaf children], and modifies his organs by distinct and full utterance, they know so well what is spoken, that it is an expression scarcely figurative to say, they hear with the eye' (Samuel Johnson, *Journey to the Western Isles of Scotland*).

Disadvantages

◆ Hearing people can hear in the dark but lipreaders cannot lipread in the dark.
◆ You need reasonably good eyesight to lipread.
◆ Lipreading is difficult unless you are lipreading your first language, e.g. an English person lipreads English better than they lipread French.
◆ Not everyone is lipreadable! Some people hardly move their lips when they talk.
◆ Some shapes look alike, for example, 'f' and 'v'.

Advantages

◆ Lipreading does not require any special equipment.
◆ Unlike a hearing aid, lipreading does not need batteries.
◆ Since most people speak, most people can be lipread.
◆ Lipreading is not expensive.
◆ You can take your lipreading ability anywhere.

When two words look similar, you can often tell which is the correct one from the context. For example:

I ate some cheese.
I ate some jeans.

Although both these sentences look alike, the first sentence is obviously the correct one.

Finally, lipreading is one of the most helpful skills that empowers a person with a hearing loss to lead an independent and fulfilled life: 'Lipreading, then, is not a cure for deafness, nor is it even a cure for all the ills of deafness, but from some of the worst ills it is a true alleviation' (Nitchie, 2004).

Notes
1 There is a copy of this most interesting book in the British Library. The RNID Library also has some very old books, which may be viewed on request.
2 An old book bought as a library throw-out. Out of print now, alas! One of his excellent books is in print, though, see reading list. Nitchie himself was deaf.
3 Contact Forest Books (see Appendix 1 for address).
4 You may have played this game at a children's party. A tray of objects is placed where everyone can see. It is left for a few minutes and then covered with a cloth. The players are then asked to write down as the names of as many of the objects on the tray as they can remember. The winner is the person who can correctly recall the highest number of objects. (The game is mentioned in Rudyard Kipling's novel, *Kim*.)
5 A true story, unfortunately!
6 For a clear understanding of lipreading read Colin Dexter's detective novel *The Silent World of Nicholas Quinn*. Colin Dexter nearly always includes a deaf or hard of hearing character somewhere in each of his Inspector Morse novels.

Lipreading exercises – student's copy

You will need:

◆   A comfortable, quiet room with good acoustics (see Chapter 11 on Acoustics).
◆   Two chairs of the same height.
◆   Good lighting.
◆   A friend or relative.

Sit facing each other. Make sure the lights are on and the curtains closed or open as necessary. The hearing person should sit with the light on their face. Turn off any background noise such as the television or radio. Your hearing friend has the 'teacher's' copy of the exercises and you have the 'student's' copy. They should take care that they do not look down or cover their mouth. It is helpful if they speak as they normally do without slowing down or exaggerating their speech as this distorts the shape of the lips.

The exercises begin with the simplest and get more challenging as they go on. Start with the first and work your way through them. Stop when you have had enough. If you feel you have had enough after one exercise, leave it there until next time.

p/b/m is a consonant shape which is usually very visible – especially at the beginnings of words. It is difficult to hear but easy to see.

Exercise 1

Which shape is 'p'? Ring the correct number.

1st   2nd   3rd

Exercise 2

At the beginning of words.

1. Pail (pale) looks like   _____   and   _____
   (In lipreading we concentrate on the shapes rather than the spelling.)

2. Poor (pore) looks like   _____   and   _____

At the end of words, the shape looks like this:

3. Cup looks like   _____   and   _____

4. Slap looks like   _____   and   _____

5. Rope looks like   _____   and   _____

Exercise 3

Watch the teacher's lips and underline the p/b/m shape when you see it.

1. Paris is the capital of France.

2. Paris is a beautiful city.

3. Paris has a population of over seven million people.

4. Paris is built on the banks of the River Seine.

5. Paris has many museums and places of interest to visit.

6. Paris was invaded by the Germans in 1940.

7. Paris has an underground system called the Metro.

8. Paris has many famous churches such as Notre Dame.

Exercise 4

One half of the sentence will give you a clue to the other half. Fill in the gaps.

1. At the Bring and Buy Sale, I bought a _____

2. At the _____ , I bought a pound of bananas.

3. At the butcher's, I bought some _____

4. At the _____ , I bought a tin of baked beans.

5. At the baker's, I bought a _____

6. At _____ , I bought a milkshake.

7. At the pet shop, I bought a box of _____

8. At the _____ , I bought a _____

    and a _____

Exercise 5

The subject of these sentences is postcards. The questions will help you to understand the passage. Read them first before you watch your teacher. When you have read them and watched your teacher, try and answer them.

1. When were postcards invented?

2. What was Emmanuel Hermann's 'title'?

3. Where did he come from?

4. How many were posted in the first three months?

5. When were postcards introduced into Britain?

6. Were they popular?

7. Where were they first on sale?

8. Who had to control the milling crowd?

Exercise 6

When two words look similar, how do you tell which is the correct word? The sense of the sentence will help you. Ring the correct word.

1. The cat sat on the mat. The cat sat on the bat.

2. I must pay the 'phone bill. I must pay the 'phone pill.

3. Put the rubbish in the pin. Put the rubbish in the bin.

4. You are my best friend. You are my pest friend.

5. Put the pan in the oven. Put the man in the oven.

6. Have you finished reading the baby? Have you finished reading the paper?

Exercise 7

It's boring/pouring.

Either of these words would make the sentence complete. How do you choose the right one? Don't panic, wait for the person to continue.

It's pouring with rain again!
It's boring, I've been waiting for ages!

Exercise 8

All these sentences are about food. Your general knowledge about food will help you supply the gaps. Watch out for the p/b/m shape.

1. I might have _____ _____ _____ for dinner.
2. I might have _____ _____ for dinner.
3. I might have _____ for dinner.
4. I might have _____ _____ _____ for dinner.
5. I might have _____'s _____ for dinner.
6. I might have _____ _____ for dinner.

Lipreading exercises – teacher's copy

- ◆ What should be said aloud is in *italic* type.
- ◆ What should be mouthed with the lips only and without the voice is in **bold** type.
- ◆ What is not spoken at all is left in normal type, like this.

Exercise 1

Look at the shape 'p'. The lips are pressed together and then they part. 'p' is a very different shape from 'f' or 'sh'. Can you tell the difference?

p
f
sh

Which is 'p'? The first shape, the second shape or the third shape? Ring the correct number.

1st   **sh**   2nd   **p**   3rd   **f**

But, 'p' looks very similar to 'b' and 'm' so that pat, bat and mat look the same, but cat, fat and rat look different.

Exercise 2

1. *Pail (pale) looks like bail (bale) and mail (male).*

   (In lipreading we concentrate on the shapes rather than the spelling.)

2. *Poor (pore) looks like boor (bore) and moor (more).*

At the end of words, the shape looks like this:

3. *Cup looks like cub and come.*

4. *Slap looks like slab and slam.*

5. *Rope looks like robe and roam.*

Exercise 3

Each sentence should be spoken two or three times using your voice.

Underline the p/b/m shape when you see it.

1. *Paris is the capital of France.*

2. *Paris is a beautiful city.*

3. *Paris has a population of over seven million people.*

4. *Paris is built on the banks of the River Seine.*

5. *Paris has many museums and places of interest to visit.*

6. *Paris was invaded by the Germans in 1940.*

7. *Paris has an underground system called the Metro.*

8. *Paris has many famous churches such as Notre Dame.*

Exercise 4

Each sentence should be spoken two or three times without using your voice. If the student cannot work out any of the words at first, give them some clues, e.g. for sentence 2:

There are nine words in the sentence.
The sentence is about bananas.
I was at the market.
One of the words is to do with weight.

One half of the sentence will give you a clue to the other half. Fill in the gaps. Each sentence begins with the words 'At the' followed by the name of a kind of shop. Each sentence contains the name of the thing I bought.

1. **At the Bring and Buy Sale, I bought a <u>paperback book</u>.**
2. **At the <u>market</u>, I bought a pound of bananas.**
3. **At the butcher's, I bought some <u>mince</u>.**
4. **At the <u>supermarket</u>, I bought a tin of baked beans.**
5. **At the baker's, I bought a <u>loaf of bread</u>.**
6. **At <u>McDonald's</u>, I bought a milkshake.**
7. **At the pet shop, I bought a box of <u>dog biscuits</u>.**
8. **At the <u>Post Office</u>, I bought a <u>postal order</u> and a <u>book of stamps</u>.**

Exercise 5

The student has some questions to answer based on these sentences. Allow plenty of time for them to read the questions through first before they try and read your lips. If you like you can tackle one question at a time. Discuss this between you.

1. **<u>Postcards</u> were invented in 1869.**
2. **They were invented <u>by</u> a <u>professor</u> called <u>Emmanuel Hermann</u>.**
3. **The <u>professor</u> was <u>from</u> Austria.**
4. **<u>More</u> than three <u>million</u> <u>postcards</u> were <u>posted</u> in the first three <u>months</u>.**
5. **<u>Postcards</u> were introduced into <u>Britain</u> in 1870.**
6. **<u>Many</u> <u>people</u> wanted to <u>buy</u> <u>them</u>.**
7. **They waited outside the <u>Post</u> Office near St <u>Paul's</u> Cathedral.**
8. **The <u>police</u> had to be called to control the <u>milling</u> crowd.**

Questions

1. When were postcards invented?
2. What was Emmanuel Hermann's 'title'?
3. Where did he come from?
4. How many were posted in the first three months?
5. When were postcards introduced into Britain?

6. Were they popular?

7. Where were they first on sale?

8. Who had to control the milling crowd?

Exercise 6

When two words look similar, how do you tell which is the correct word? The sense of the sentence will help you. Ring the correct word.

1. **The cat sat on the mat. The cat sat on the bat.**

2. **I must pay the 'phone bill. I must pay the phone pill.**

3. **Put the rubbish in the pin. Put the rubbish in the bin.**

4. **You are my best friend. You are my pest friend.**

5. **Put the pan in the oven. Put the man in the oven.**

6. **Have you finished reading the baby? Have you finished reading the paper?**

Exercise 7

It's boring/pouring.

Either of these words would make the sentence complete. How do you choose the right one? Don't panic, wait for the person to continue.

It's pouring with rain again!
It's boring, I've been waiting for ages!

Exercise 8

All these sentences are about food. Your memory will help you supply the gaps.

1. **I might have beans on toast for dinner.**

2. **I might have roast beef for dinner.**

3. **I might have pizza for dinner.**

4. **I might have steak and kidney pudding for dinner.**

5. **I might have shepherd's pie for dinner.**

6. **I might have pork chops for dinner.**

Chapter 8

Non-verbal communication: body language and face reading

When you interact with others your words make up only 30–35% of your communication, and when you converse with another person you are letting them know things about yourself in ways you would never imagine without even saying a word.

Understanding what is going on between people often depends on interpreting non-verbal communication. Have you ever sat in a room and known that there is an underlying animosity between two people, because one person is crossing their legs at the knee away from the person sitting next to them? Have you ever been with someone you know likes you and you like them too? Have you noticed how they listen attentively to what you are saying, and smile, and nod their head when in agreement with you? Because you are paying favourable and alert attention to people when you are with them, they appear pleased that you are so interested in what they are saying, little knowing that you are having to concentrate hard to understand because of your hearing loss.

When you have a hearing loss, however slight, non-verbal communication can often provide you with a range of clues about what is going on. It is a well-known fact that President Bush walks like a man with a purpose; his arms move across his body, his fists are slightly clenched and he looks confident. If the camera is trained on a person who is just stepping into the public gaze, have you noticed how men check the knot in their tie and women smooth their hair? This self-grooming is an instinctive gesture that we make to check that our outward appearance will create a favourable impression.

Next time you are sitting at a table look at the people around you. Sitting with your arms folded on the table and leaning forward denotes interest and a comradely feeling to those nearby, whereas sitting leaning back from the table with arms folded can denote, amongst other things, a lack of interest or a need to be more comfortable.

The police have picked up on the importance of body language by suggesting that, in order to appear more confident and in control, especially at night, we should walk in the light at all times at a rapid pace with our heads held high, and look as though we know where we are going. We should remember too to keep our hands free – and not walk about with them in our pockets!

Non-verbal communication also includes face reading. Many people with a hearing loss say that lipreading is helpful, but face reading is a more appropriate term because clues are gained from observing the whole face.

During a television programme about Stalin a person who had been sent to work in the gulags was describing the privations they had endured. They had obviously been exposed to situations that most of us only have nightmares about, but their face belied their experience as they had well-defined laughter lines happily fanning out from the outer corner of each eye like rays from the sun. It would appear that they were naturally optimistic and perhaps this had helped their survival.

A person with thin lips is not only difficult to lipread but it has also been suggested that they may have a short, terse way of doing things. Also a person with a wide face and convex nose makes a natural leader and excels at challenges. A person with wide set eyes may be a magical multitasker. To seek out a person who pays attention to detail and dislikes interruptions, observe if they have close-set eyes.

Many experts on the study of body language advocate that if you want to know how a person is feeling, you should look at their feet first. Studies on body language tell us that we have less control over what actions we make below our waist; so the lower part of our body becomes most important if we want to know something about someone else's emotions or intentions. For instance, when someone gets anxious, the ways in which they move, contract and twitch their feet are emotional mood leaks, even if other parts of their body make them appear self-confident. When standing up, they express apprehension, anxiety or hurry by orientating one foot in the direction of the exit, showing in this way their uneasiness and intention to escape.

Interpreting body language

General posture

The whole body turned away may mean that the person does not want to communicate. When accessing visual information, the person will tend to look up, straighten up their body, and make gestures into space. When accessing auditory information, they will tend to look to the side, maybe slant their head and cross their arms, and their knees will generally be pointing in the direction of whatever is interesting them. When accessing a person's whole body or individual muscular movements, they will tend to look down and slump over.

Reading if a person is anxious

- Not looking at you
- Throat-clearing
- Fidgeting
- Hands covering mouth
- Tugging at clothes
- Index finger pulling collar from neck
- Jingling things in pockets
- Ear-tugging
- Hand-wringing
- Sweating
- Glances at exit door
- Taking a step back

Reading if a person is being open

- Open body posture
- Smiling
- Repeating glances

Reading if a person is being interested

- Leaning forward
- Facing you directly
- Tilting head
- Sitting on edge of chair
- Hand-to-face gestures
- Smiling
- Grooming behaviour
- Moistening lips
- Playing with hair or clothes
- Picking lint off your jacket

- Touching you briefly
- Tapping foot to music as you pass

Reading if a person is evaluating you

- Hand-to-face gestures
- Stroking chin
- Head tilted
- Holding glasses' earpiece to mouth
- Pacing
- Hand to bridge of nose
- Squinting

Reading if a person is feeling territorial or dominant

- Feet up
- Leaning against object
- Moving things around on table
- Standing or leaning over you
- Hands behind head, leaning back

Interpreting face language

Although it might appear a crude way to gain clues about a situation, what cartoonists do is to pick out the essential features and expressions of a person and capture them in just a few lines. When we first mention lipreading to a patient they invariably become very negative about their ability to do it. People who have experienced a loss of hearing for many years are often not aware how they understand speech until we explain the results of their audiogram and how this affects their ability to discriminate speech sounds and visual clues. Many people say they do not lipread, they face read. For example, a profoundly deaf acquaintance reminded me several years ago that they knew if someone was going to be helpful in a task that required perfection if they noticed the outer corner of the eye was lower than the inner corner.

It is not the purpose of this book to define all aspects of face language. It would prove an onerous task as the face can make 43 distinct muscular movements – in a study at the University of California, 3000 expressions that comprise the essential repertoire of human facial displays of emotion were identified. Many of us learn to interpret intuitively facial movements in someone we are familiar with, and perhaps without thinking prepare ourselves to respond appropriately.

The human face is often used as an image in the English language, which is filled with expressions such as 'starry-eyed' (which incidentally means to be full of fantasies and have a lot of impractical ideas).

We have understood from our patients that face watching is more important than lipreading and we hope that those facial features we have included will, at a glance, give you some idea what character and temperament you might expect from the person you are with.

Eyes – 'the window of the soul'

- Clear bright gleaming eyes – a good night's sleep, good health, happiness and liveliness.
- Dull eyes – a person may be ill, tired or stressed.
- Red eyes – has been working too long on a computer, recently been upset or is experiencing ill health.
- Direct gaze – honest, caring and interested.

- Fidgety gaze – disinterested, insecure, impatient.
- Reflective gaze – really listening and mirroring the speaker's emotions.
- Downward gaze – can mean a defeated attitude or shyness. It may also reflect guilt, shame, or submissiveness, as when distorting the truth or telling a lie.

Lips – the mouth moves with the thoughts and mirrors a person's inner emotions.

- Trembling lips – unhappy.
- Biting a lip – pensive.
- Compressed lips – indicate the onset of anger or sadness or annoyance.
- Pouting lips – sadness or uncertainty.
- Pursed lips – disagreement, scheming, or calculated thought.
- Finally, when people are happy, their lips are open in a smile allowing the viewer to see the clues from their teeth. A wide gap can depict a sunny personality. Not many people know that!

Chapter 9

Levels of hearing

- ◆ When someone coughs, do you regard it as just a noise in the background, or is it a sound warning you that someone is behind you or that they have a cold?
- ◆ Is birdsong something that gives you pleasure, or is it just background noise?
- ◆ Is a person talking about something you recognise and are easily able to understand, or is it just a warning sound alerting you to the fact that a person is in the room?

When you experience a loss of hearing you may lose the ability to hear sound on several or all of the different levels which you possibly took for granted when your hearing was unimpaired and normal. Perhaps you gave little thought to how we use our hearing until you began to realise that you were missing parts of words, and were unable to hear the door or telephone bell ring until someone told you. It may well be that you have felt slightly anxious and depressed because, not only have you been unable to hear the warning sounds of life, but also the small sounds that enhanced your feeling of well-being, such as rain on the window and wind in the trees, or the comforting sound of the fridge turning on and off.

In our clinical and personal experience, we have discovered that explaining these levels of sound to a person who is learning to adjust to amplification and at the same time having their auditory memory activated enables them to develop a different understanding about the importance of receiving sound and the reason for this. We hope that knowledge of these levels of missed sound will enable you to gain a deeper understanding of why you may have experienced feelings of depression, anxiety and uncertainty since you lost your hearing. It may also offer an insight as to why it is crucial that you follow the advice of the hearing professional who issued you with a hearing aid. Hearing aids and cochlear implants can often enable you to understand speech better; restore a sound you enjoy; enable you to comprehend if a person is happy or sad; alert you to the sound of the door bell or the 'phone ringing; and comfort you by giving you back a feeling of being in touch with everyday sounds.

These levels of hearing were first noticed at the close of World War II by Dr Ramsdell while he was working in Deshon Army Hospital in Butler, Pennsylvania, which was a Veteran's Administration Hospital. He had the opportunity to observe young adults who had lost some or all of their hearing whilst on active service, and recognised the four stages of how we use our hearing, particularly the importance of the 'feeling of oneness with an active environment'. These young adults constantly complained that that the world seemed dead. Doctor Ramsdell became aware that we rely on our hearing for:

- ◆ understanding speech – *the symbolic level*;
- ◆ appreciating sounds that please us – *the aesthetic level*;
- ◆ recognising sounds that alert us – *the warning level*, and
- ◆ recognising the changing background sounds of the world around us – *the primitive level*.

Since reading about his work we have become conscious through our personal and clinical observations that we also use our hearing at another level. We are helped in our understanding of speech by recognising the quality and intonation of a sound, and we have called this the *tonal level.*

Levels of hearing

The first level is the *symbolic,* or *speech,* level, which informs, educates and entertains us. It enriches human life and enables us to communicate our experience through a complex medium. It permits us to clarify and organise our thoughts and formalise social prohibitions, e.g. turn taking in conversations.

The second level is the *aesthetic* level, which gives us pleasure from sounds such as music, the sound of the sea, a cat purring, or rain on the window.

The third level is the *tonal* level, which is responsible for the quality and character of a sound. It is at this level that we also hear the accent, dialect, intonation and modulation of a voice, as well as the stress in a voice that lets us know that a person is continuing to speak.

The fourth level is the *signal,* or *warning,* level, at which we receive a direct sign or signal of events to which we make constant adjustments, e.g. the sound of a door opening or footsteps alerts us to the need to be prepared for another person entering the room or coming up behind us.

The fifth level is the *background,* or *primitive,* level, which provides an auditory background for daily living. This is the most fundamental level of the hearing function and is the most emotionally connected with the difficulties that you may occasionally experience, e.g. when the battery in your hearing aid is flat and you are unable to hear, which in turn gives rise to feelings of anxiety.

All these levels are prominent at different times, depending on the attention being paid to them for information, security, feelings of well-being and understanding the spoken word.

The two boxes below are examples of the attention we may pay to what we hear and how we interpret the sound for our information or safety and our relation to the world somewhere below the level of clear consciousness and perception.

> You are sitting in a room near an open window which looks out onto a busy road. The sound of traffic is comforting or irritating depending on your reaction to the noise. All the same you know you can hear it. You remember that you have forgotten something for a meal you are making and you decide to drive to a local shop. You pay more attention to the traffic noise to check how busy the road is – the loudness of the sound changes and you know that there is heavy traffic on the road, which therefore warns you to leave more time for your journey. Driving the car out of the driveway you hear a siren and know that you will need to wait before you leave the drive. This is because the sound of the siren is meaningful and symbolic. What was originally a comforting background sound has become first a warning sound, and then a symbolic sound, depending on your individual need to understand the sound.

> You are sitting in a park enjoying the spring sunshine and talking companionably with a friend. The babble of noise created by nearby children, dogs, birds and a lawnmower are comforting and reassuring. Occasionally some sounds warn you that something is happening, but you only pay attention when you need to be aware of them, for example if a ball is coming towards you. Your friend's voice changes as they tell you some good news and changes again when they explain that it will mean a lot of work. The sound of low flying aircraft warns you that you are in the flight path of a nearby airport. You both return to companionable silence as you think about the conversation you are having and the sounds of aircraft, children, dogs and the lawnmower recede into the background. You are glad your hearing aid is providing you with some reassuring sound.

What can restore these levels of hearing?

Symbolic or speech level – for information, education, entertainment

- DVDs
- Hearing aids
- Information boards
- Internet
- Text televisions
- Text telephones
- Newspapers
- Lipreading
- Amplifiers on hand-held and mobile phones
- Inductive couplers
- Spectacles
- STAGETEXT
- Subtitled films
- Computers
- Video recorders that record subtitles
- Books

Aesthetic level – music and art appreciation

- Amplifiers on hand-held and mobile phones
- DVDs
- Hearing aids
- Spectacles
- STAGETEXT
- Subtitled television and films
- Text televisions
- Written information in art galleries and before a concert

Tonal level

- Hearing aids

Signal or warning level – to let you know that a door is shutting, a bell ringing or a person shouting

- Vibrotactile devices
- Flashing, vibrating alerting systems
- Hearing aids
- Hearing Dogs[1]
- Louder/different tone of alerting systems
- Spectacles
- Text indicators

Background or primitive level – clock ticking, wind, bird song, murmur of voices

- Hearing aids
- Hearing Dogs
- STAGETEXT
- Subtitled television and films
- Vibrotactile devices

Notes

1 Hearing Dogs are trained to respond to up to five sounds. They then alert their owner by touching them and indicating the source of the sound. A simple, gentle gesture that can open up a sometimes isolated and silent world or even save a life.

Chapter 10

Dos and don'ts for hearing aid users

About deafness I know everything and nothing.

David Wright, 1969

There are many different causes of hearing loss. There are many different reactions to hearing loss. Hearing loss is not selective, it can affect people of both sexes, all ages, all classes and all nationalities. People are all different. While some of us are naturally cheerful, others are life's pessimists. Some of us have supportive families, others live alone. For this reason, there cannot ever be a definitive book about deafness. The coping strategies that work well for some people may not work as well for others. This book is not so much a box of chocolates (where someone has chosen the sweets for you) as the 'pick and mix' sweet counter (where you choose the sweets that you like best). You select the morsels that you find helpful, but be adventurous – try a new flavour from time to time!

Here are a few things that can make life much easier.

Be kind to your hearing aid

Many hearing aids lead rather sad and lonely lives in people's handbags and pockets. They are not worn much, if at all, and they are not cared for. Hearing aids do not work if they are not worn. They may not always do what you hope they can (see Chapter 5 on Realistic expectations) but they cannot do anything if they are not used at all. People who have a car do not usually leave it in the garage all the time without using it. Drivers also know that it needs fuel, the occasional repair, a bit of cleaning, an MOT every year and some tender love and care. Well so do hearing aids!

If you wear your hearing aid on a regular daily basis you will find that you gradually hear better with it. It takes time for the average person to adjust to a new hearing aid – around three months. (Some people, of course, adapt much faster than others.) This is because we do not just hear with the ear, but the brain also. For most people, losing their hearing is a gradual process. They do not suddenly become hard of hearing. Just as your hair does not usually go grey overnight, but gradually, so your hearing gradually becomes dulled. The brain becomes used to living in a rather quiet, 'muffled' world. When you start wearing a hearing aid for the first time, it can be rather a shock. Suddenly you are hearing sounds you may not have heard before. Suddenly you are hearing sounds that you used to hear but have not heard for years. The brain needs time to learn to understand and interpret sounds all over again. So, start wearing it for half an hour a day in a quiet room such as your living room (see Chapter 11 on Acoustics) and gradually increase both the amount of time you wear it and the kind of environment you listen in. (See the section below on *Learning to wear a hearing aid*.)

The fuel

When you received your hearing aid, your local Audiology Department/Private Dispenser will have given you information about how to obtain new batteries for it.

Hearing aid batteries are currently provided free of charge for all NHS hearing aids (but not for private ones). Well-known high-street chemists also sell hearing aid batteries. It is sensible to make sure that you do not run out of these. Many hearing aid users always carry spare batteries with them everywhere they go. Some hearing aids give a warning when the battery is fading, but many do not and just suddenly cut out. If you are going somewhere important and do not want to change your hearing aid battery while you are out, just put a new one in before you leave home. It is worth opening the battery compartments at night to allow any moisture to dry out.

A hearing aid battery may last for up to a month but the more powerful the hearing aid, the faster it will use up batteries. Since hearing aid batteries are air-activated, they begin to work as soon as the coloured sticker on the back is removed. This means that, if you do not wear your hearing aid for a while, the battery will continue to run down even if the aid has been switched off. Make sure that you have enough batteries to last you when you are away on holiday and when the hospital department/hearing aid dispenser is closed, e.g. over a Bank Holiday weekend or on public holidays. Some departments will loan you a spare hearing aid to take with you on holiday.

Repairs, MOT and cleaning

The Audiology Department/Dispenser will also have told you how to arrange to have your hearing aid repaired. Hearing aids need the tubing, which connects the ear mould (the bit that goes in the ear) to the actual hearing aid (the bit that goes behind the ear), replaced about every six months to a year. It is a good idea, therefore, to arrange to have your hearing aid retubed and checked once a year, thus lessening the chances of it breaking down at an inconvenient moment. Cleaning the hearing aid is done by detaching the earpiece and tubing from the hearing aid and running the earpiece and tubing only under the tap. (See the section below on *How to look after your hearing aid.*)

> When living with a disability, it often helps to keep two very important things – a sense of humour and a sense of proportion. Being deaf is not funny, but it has its funny side. One of our patients recently bought a clock for the bedroom. She did not want an alarm clock, she just wanted to be able to tell the time when she woke up. So she chose an attractive little clock with a nice clear face and hands that she could see, even when she took her glasses off. That night her husband, who is hearing, said, 'That clock ticks.' Of course, our patient had no idea that the clock ticked.

Some dos and don'ts

Do

- Be positive
- Be sensible
- Take advice
- Be patient
- Have a life
- Develop an interest in an absorbing hobby

- Be assertive
- Use anger in a positive way
- Be prepared for prejudice and misunderstanding
- Educate ignorance
- Look for opportunities
- Make time for yourself – deafness is tiring
- Be realistic – don't continually set yourself up to fail, e.g. phone calls, taking minutes at meetings
- Challenge yourself – set goals
- Try anyway
- Keep things in proportion

Don't

- Don't forget batteries and repairs
- Don't forget spare hearing aid for your holiday
- Don't blame yourself
- Don't use it to get out of things you don't want to do
- Don't use it to control others
- Don't withdraw

Learning to wear a hearing aid

- Take each stage in your own time. It does not matter if each stage takes you hours, days, weeks, months or years.
- Pass on to the next stage when you feel ready.
- Practise every day. If you were to break a leg, the physiotherapist would give you exercises to perform every day – once a week would not help you get the use of your leg back. You need to wear your hearing aid for part of every day to get the most benefit from it.
- It is not advisable to wear your hearing aid in bed or in the bath or shower.
- Please read Chapter 5 on Realistic expectations. Hearing aids are simply aids to hearing and not ears!

Stage 1

Wear your hearing aid in a quiet room with good acoustics (such as your living room). Make sure you are on your own and feeling relaxed. Wear it for about half an hour a day. Then take it out.

What sounds can you hear in a quiet room when you have your hearing aid in? Remember, most people who are getting a hearing aid for the first time, have a mild or moderate hearing loss. Depending on the degree and nature of your hearing loss (and where you live), you may be able to hear some of the following:

- clock ticking
- central heating gurgling
- the next-door neighbours (footsteps, television, etc.)
- traffic in the street
- car doors slamming
- front doorbell
- telephone ringing
- smoke alarm
- newspaper rustling.

Make your own list of the sounds you can hear. You may be surprised! If you cannot hear the doorbell, the television, the smoke alarm or the telephone, see Appendix 1 Useful Addresses for stockists of special equipment.

When you feel comfortable with this stage, move on to Stage 2.

Stage 2

Wear your hearing aid for one hour a day. Visit other rooms in your home. Try turning switches on and off. Go into the kitchen, turn the taps on and listen to the water running. (Remember to turn the taps off!) Flush the lavatory. Open and shut doors. Does the world seem a noisier place than you remembered?

◆ Did you notice that the sounds seem louder and harsher in the kitchen and bathroom?

◆ What kinds of sounds are more noticeable than others?

◆ Can you hear sounds that you could not hear before you got your hearing aid?

When you feel comfortable with this stage, move on to Stage 3.

Stage 3

Wear your hearing aid for two hours a day. Try some of the following:

◆ Wear your hearing aid in the garden or in a local park or anywhere fairly quiet and out of doors.

◆ Hold a conversation indoors with a family member or friend or someone you know well. (Remember to turn off the TV or radio, face the speaker and make sure the light is good.)

◆ Watch the news on the television. Newsreaders are often easier to hear because the look directly at the camera, speak clearly and enunciate distinctly. They do not usually talk over background noise. If this is difficult, switch on the subtitles (see Chapter 12 on Access to information).

When you feel comfortable with this stage, move on to Stage 4.

Stage 4

Wear your hearing aid for four hours a day. Try to wear it in some of the following situations:

◆ a trip to your local newsagent to buy a paper

◆ somewhere that you go regularly, where you know some of the people, e.g. doctor's surgery, library, lunch club, place of worship, local club or society, evening class, lipreading class, day centre, voluntary organisation, workplace

◆ watching television, listening to the radio/CDs/talking books, etc.

When you feel comfortable with this stage, move on to Stage 5.

Stage 5

Wear your hearing aid for as many hours a day as you feel comfortable with. Now try wearing it:

◆ in the car, or on the bus, or on a train

◆ talking to strangers or people you do not know well

◆ in the town/city/village/High Street

◆ when using the telephone (see Chapter 13).

Congratulations! You are now a regular hearing aid user.

More dos and don'ts

Dos

◆ Coping with noise can be tiring, especially when you are not used to it. You may find you need to 'take a break' each day to rest your ears and your brain. It is helpful to alert those around you when you have taken your hearing aids out; otherwise they will assume that you can still hear them.

◆ If you use hair spray, remember to spray your hair before you put your hearing aid(s) in. Hairspray damages hearing aids.

◆ Tell your hairdresser/barber that you will need to take your hearing aids out before he/she does your hair. Discuss how you will communicate in the mean-time, e.g. pad and pen.

◆ Look very carefully before you cross the road. It is very difficult to judge where sound is coming from if you are a hearing aid user.

Don'ts

◆ Do not wear your hearing aid in bed. This is uncomfortable, and having the ear blocked all the time can cause ear infections. If you are worried that you will not be able to hear certain sounds at night, such as the smoke alarm, see the Appendix 1 Useful Addresses for stockists of special equipment.

◆ Do not wear your hearing aid in the bath, shower, when you wash your hair or go swimming. Water does not agree with hearing aids. (It is quite safe to wear them in the rain, except perhaps in a torrential downpour!)

◆ Do not leave your hearing aid(s) in your ears while they are switched off. This will mean that you are effectively walking around with earplugs in. No sound will be able to get through at all and this could be dangerous. Always switch your hearing aids off and take them out.

How to look after your hearing aid

◆ To get the best sound out of your hearing aid, it is sensible to take good care of it.

◆ Have your hearing aid checked regularly by your audiologist – at least annually.

◆ Take a spare hearing aid with you when you go on holiday – if this is possible.

◆ Always carry spare hearing aid batteries.

◆ Clean the ear mould (the piece that goes in your ear) and the tubing (the tube that connects the ear mould to the hearing aid) regularly. Detach the earpiece and tubing from the hearing aid (ask your audiologist to show you how to do this) and run it under the tap. Warm water is best. Do not use soap or detergent because these can irritate the ear. Leave the earpiece and tubing to dry.

◆ Make sure the earpiece is not blocked with wax. Wax stops the sound from getting through. Wax can be removed from the hole at the end of the earpiece using a pin (a quilting pin is perfect for the job).

◆ Make sure the tubing is not blocked with condensation. Condensation looks like little bubbles and will prevent the sound getting through. To remove it, detach the ear mould and tubing from the hearing aid and blow through it using a 'puffer' (available from firms such as Connevans (see Appendix 1). Using your breath to blow through it could make the problem worse, because your breath is moist, but it is better to do this than nothing at all.

- The tubing should be soft and flexible. If it has become hard it will affect the quality of the sound your hear. Ask your audiologist to replace the tubing or ask him/her to teach you how to replace it yourself.
- When you have finished wearing your hearing aid for the day, switch it off, take it out, wipe the earpiece with a clean tissue (or baby wipe) and store it in its box. This is very important. Hearing aids are expensive and easily damaged but are less likely to be broken if they are put away safely.
- Keep your hearing aid out of the reach of children and dogs. Children love to play with them and dogs like to eat them.

Problems with hearing aids

Is your hearing aid whistling?

A well-fitting hearing aid that is working properly should not whistle. Whistling can be caused by:

- *The hearing aid not being put in the ear properly*. Make sure the audiologist teaches you how to do this before you leave after having your first hearing aid fitted.
- *The ear mould not fitting correctly*. The human ear continues to grow and change shape. The ear mould which fitted you five years ago may not fit you now. You might need a new ear mould. Ask your audiologist.
- *The tubing being cracked or defective*. Ask your audiologist to replace it.
- *The ear being blocked with wax*. Ask your doctor to check your ears for wax and follow his directions.
- *The hearing aid being at full-volume*. Hearing aids are normally worn below full volume. If you find that you need to turn your hearing aid on full all the time (instead of very occasionally), it may be because your hearing aid is defective or because you need a stronger hearing aid. See your audiologist.
- *The shape of the ear*. Occasionally it is difficult to get an ear mould fitting as snugly as possible because of the shape of the ear.

Is your hearing aid not working?

If your hearing aid is not working, it is worth checking the following before going to see your audiologist. It may save you a wasted journey!

- Is the hearing aid switched on? (Sorry, but we see this every day!)
- Does the battery need replacing? Replace the battery.
- Is the ear mould blocked with wax? Unblock the ear mould using a pin.
- Does the ear mould need cleaning? Clean the ear mould with warm water as directed.
- Is the tubing blocked with wax? Unblock the tubing using a puffer as directed.
- Does the tubing need replacing? Replace the tubing.
- Is your ear blocked with wax or infection? Your ear may feel uncomfortable or it may hurt. If you have tinnitus, it may be louder. See your doctor.

Remember, if in doubt, see your audiologist!

Checklist

Can you put your hearing aid in?	**YES/NO**
Does it feel comfortable?	**YES/NO**

Can you switch it on and off and find the loop switch?   **YES/NO**

Can you change the battery?   **YES/NO**

Can you clean the earpiece?   **YES/NO**

If the answer to any of these questions is 'NO', go back to your audiologist for help. Your hearing aid may feel a little strange at first – just like new shoes or new glasses do – but it should not hurt your ear or make it sore or bleed.

Fitting your ear mould

Many people experience difficulties fitting their ear mould when they first receive a hearng aid.

To practise putting your ear mould in your ear yourself, go through the following steps:

1. If you can, have the ear mould inserted correctly in your ear by the technician, a family member or friend.
2. Put your index finger to your ear and feel how the ear mould is sitting in your ear. Feel how the top of the ear mould fits underneath the top of the ear and is not poking out.
3. Lever out the back curve of your ear mould using your thumb. **Do not pull the ear mould completely out of the ear.** Concentrate on what the ear mould feels like as it is dislodged from your ear. Repeat this procedure twice.
4. Remove the ear mould completely by grasping it between your thumb and index finger. **Do not let go**. Then place it back in your ear. Repeat this procedure once.
5. Remove the ear mould and hearing aid from your ear. Look at how you are holding it and put it back. Repeat this procedure once.
6. Remove the ear mould and hearing aid from your ear and place it on the table. **Do not let go**. Replace the ear mould in your ear and the hearing aid behind the ear.
7. Finally, remove the ear mould and hearing aid from your ear. Place it on the table. Leave it there. Then pick it up and put the ear mould in your ear and hearing aid behind your ear.

For future reference, pick the ear mould up between your thumb and finger, grasping the back prong like you would the handle on a cup.

Chapter 11

Acoustics

To make sure that your listening experiences are satisfying it may help to be prepared for environmental situations that are out of your control. For example, have you noticed you find it easier to understand the spoken word best in your own home, and dread the thought of having a meal in a restaurant? When you are travelling and take the train to an airport, have you noticed the sound at the airport does not seem as strident as in the railway station?

Even the best hearing aids will not cope satisfactorily in surroundings where the acoustics are poor. You may have discovered that it is difficult, and sometimes painful, to concentrate on listening to speech if there is a lot of background noise. Troublesome echoes may frequently occur in an area where the ceiling is concave in shape and highly reflective of sound. In a railway station the walls are frequently concrete and there are many glass windows, whereas in an airport the floors may be carpeted, and the ceilings not always so high.

> Shortly after Sir Charles Barry completed building the House of Commons in 1851 Members of Parliament complained about the acoustics and he had to lower the roof, after which he refused to enter the building again.

In difficult listening situations you may find it easier to turn your hearing aids down and rely on your residual hearing and lipreading because the signal-to-noise ratio of speech, which is the relationship between the input signal (such as speech) and the background noise, is too great.

Electronically produced sound echoing in an open space makes understanding many public announcements impossible, even for people with normal hearing. It is one of the areas in the public domain that sound engineers are continuously striving to correct.

Sound travels and behaves very differently in an enclosed space than it does out of doors because of the reverberation time, which is the measurement of how long it takes for sound to decay or break up. When it is very long it becomes a noticeable echo, as in a gymnasium when the benches, walls and ceilings cause sound waves to bounce back. On the other hand the acoustics of a large auditorium may be very different when it is full from when it is empty, because unoccupied seats reflect sound, whereas an audience absorbs sound.

The saying 'forewarned is forearmed' is particularly true if you are wearing a hearing aid. Try to be prepared for difficult listening situations. You should mentally prepare yourself for making an extra effort to understand what is being said in some situations, and know that there will be other opportunities to relax and make the most of your hearing aid. With this in mind we have compiled a list of favourable and unfavourable listening conditions for hearing aid users. It is the result of many years of interaction personally and professionally with family, friends, colleagues and students and noticing how differently the hearing aid acts in a variety of locations.

Conditions for hearings aid users

Favourable

[Sound is absorbed and there is minimum environmental noise]

◆ Sandy *beaches* that deaden footfalls – if the tide is out the sound of the waves will not be so loud.

◆ *Climatic conditions* such as still weather when there is no wind to be picked up by the microphone of the hearing aid. In the winter snow muffles and absorbs sound.

◆ *Hillsides and parks* where there are fewer obstacles to reflect the sound waves back to the listener. There is often less background noise too.

◆ *Woods* where the trees act as wind breaks and the carpet of dead leaves muffle footsteps. These conditions get the most out of the input of a hearing aid.

◆ *Department stores* with fashion, furnishing and haberdashery departments where the fabrics have a high absorption of sound.

◆ *Hotels* that have carpeted public areas with deep armchairs. These are ideal because not only is the sound deadened but the chairs can often be pulled around for listeners to face each other, which may be helpful for lipreading. They may also have subdued music.

◆ *Libraries*, which used to be quiet because speaking aloud was forbidden, but are now – and rightly so – a place for young children to learn to read and develop all important new computer skills. However, they still remain inherently quiet, because any sound is absorbed by the books or the carpets.

◆ *Museums* afford a peaceful haven if they are relatively small, the exception being museums which have activities for children.

◆ *Offices* that are carpeted and have felt-covered room dividers, which act as buffers to the speech disturbance caused by workers in near and distant work stations, ventilation and office equipment.

◆ *Public access areas* such as rooms with actively absorbent surfaces such as thickly curtained windows, double glazing, carpeted floors, table covers, wooden wall panelling, wallpaper that is thick or has a polystyrene underlay – all of these are effectively absorbent. Acoustic tiles, baffles or drapes suspended from the ceiling and fabric faced wall panels are all helpful.

> There is a delightful café in York railway station, built mostly from wood and with drapes suspended from the ceiling. The tables are in small clusters near the window and there is very little interference from the noise of the trains as they enter and leave the station. Val said it was easier to understand speech in this comfortable area.

◆ *Public houses* that limit the use of music and where the game machines are away from the public area.

◆ *Quiet streets* where there is little through traffic. The traffic noise in London is notorious, but just behind Oxford Street and Kensington High Street there are many small streets, which offer an alternative haven to this incessant cacophony of sound.

◆ *Residential living rooms and bedrooms* with soft furnishings.

- *Restaurants* that are carpeted and do not have loud background music or a piano playing.
- *Transport vehicles* such as Intercity trains, and some cars and taxis, and also buses and ships where the engine is muffled and passengers and upholstered seats absorb sound.

Unfavourable

- Sound reflecting off *hard surfaces* causing reverberation. High levels of intrusive ambient noise are present, such as extraneous noise transmitted from adjacent areas, through walls, ceilings, door and windows; and noise from ventilation systems.
- *Beaches* that are pebbled or shingled are noisier, because of the scrunch of footsteps and the noise made by pebbles crashing against each other, especially if the sea is rough.
- *Climatic conditions* such as the sound of wind through the microphone of the hearing aid. Rain causes wet road conditions and traffic noise is increased because of the sound of tyres on the asphalt. Normally soft areas of land can be hardened by frost causing more rebound of sounds.
- *Metal roofs* that reflect high frequency sound so that rain falling on them produces high background noise levels.
- *Public access areas* that are cube shaped. According to the model design theory, the worst possible room shape is a cube such as many hotel lobbies, classrooms, hospital waiting rooms, railway stations, supermarkets, kitchens, and open plan offices. All have many hard surfaces where sound travels and behaves differently. Sound waves bounce back or reverberate. Many have high ceilings, metal frame-work supported by concrete or stone pillars.
- *Residential kitchens* with stainless steel, copper, ceramic tile, granite or marble work surfaces. Kitchen appliances can create background noise, such as the spinning drum of a washing machine.
- *Restaurants* that favour the contemporary fashion of large, often single-glazed, windows covered with horizontal or vertical Venetian or woven wood blinds. Formica or glass topped tables and floors made of hard wood, brick, tile, flagstone, slate, natural stone, river rock, marble or granite chips.
- *Transport vehicles* such as smaller local buses and trains where the extraneous traffic noise is not adequately reduced because windows need to be left open.
- *Tunnels* that are narrow with high ceilings and built from stone or concrete with flagged floors.

Tips
If you find listening to conversation in your kitchen difficult, think about making the following changes:
- thick cloth or place mats for the table
- table cloth with a felt underlay
- carpet or soft linoleum on the floor
- double glazing (for reducing external noise)
- curtains
- individual foam mats on work surfaces
- turning off the radio or TV during meal times
- using time switches for the washing machine and dishwasher to come on at night.

Good environment   *Bad environment*

Quiz

Maximise the use of a hearing aid by knowing where to choose to have the best listening experience!

1. You have invited a friend for a meal – where would you sit?
   a. in the lounge   ❑
   b. in the kitchen   ❑

2. You need to speak to the manager of a supermarket – where would you ask to see him?
   a. in the centre of the store   ❑
   b. in a corner of the store   ❑
   c. in his office   ❑

3. You are walking with a friend in a busy street and she has something to tell you – where and when would you suggest you stop to have a conversation?
   a. when you get home   ❑
   b. just inside a shop doorway   ❑
   c. in a side street or lane   ❑
   d. when you are waiting to cross the road at the traffic lights   ❑

4. You want to meet a friend for afternoon tea – where would you suggest you meet?
   a. in the café of a supermarket   ❑
   b. in a fast food outlet   ❑
   c. in a small café with modern fitments   ❑
   d. in the lounge of a hotel   ❑
   e. in a small teashop, which you know has carpeting   ❑

5. You are meeting a friend at the railway station and you are taking a taxi to your home because she is carrying heavy luggage – where would you have a conversation with her?
   a. in the station   ❑
   b. waiting for the taxi   ❑
   c. in the taxi   ❑

Answers to Quiz

1a; 2c; 3a, b, c; 4d, e; 5c

Chapter 12

Access to information

> Retaining independence, dignity and freedom through communication and information technology.

Experiencing a hearing loss may undermine your confidence in all forms of communication. Many people find problems when they visit the doctor's surgery – they try hard to lipread what the doctor is saying, and if possible listen to him as well; they also repeat some of the words back to check if they have understood properly, but later on they become worried that they might have misunderstood after all, because the conditions were not ideal. For example, the doctor's back may have been to the light.

A similar difficulty could occur after a visit to a place of special interest or to the theatre. You may have become exhausted because of the effort required to understand verbally presented information. Perhaps as a result you decided to avoid live entertainment because the experience was unsatisfactory and not worth the investment of time and money.

> When she gave the introductory presentation at a function highlighting the needs of deaf and hard of hearing people to enable them to access the arts at a well known London gallery, Laraine Callow, Chair of Hearing Concern, said, 'Inadequate access to the arts is like a frame without a picture.' She was referring to guided tours that take place without a sign language interpreter, lipspeaker, or the use of radio aids and loop or infrared induction systems.

Fortunately, the increasing use of information technology has changed the way we are put in the picture about what is happening. It is no longer always necessary to use the sense of hearing to understand speech in order to be informed, educated and entertained on the telephone or TV. Two popular examples are the availability of text messaging (SMS – short message system) and email to provide access to telecommunications, and of subtitles on a wide variety of TV programmes, DVDs (Digital Versatile Discs) and videos.

Other choices are ever widening, and the prices dropping, as we write this book. This is expected to continue as the demand for faster and more visual communication grows in our global society. As a result of 3G technology (Third Generation technology) you can now watch video clips and hold a video conversation on your mobile phone (if you are lucky enough to have a decent signal).

We remember when 'snail mail' was the only way to ensure that a vital message arrived on time, and that was always at the mercy of the vagaries of the postal service.

We have collaborated on writing this book by emailing drafts to each other. We have used our mobile phones to ensure we are meeting at the correct time and place, thus avoiding the stress caused by uncertainty, which has in turn has increased our confidence in communication.

> A good example of our use of modern technology was when we had arranged to spend two days together in York, which is equidistant from both our homes, to work on this book. Unfortunately, Val was delayed and had to let Bunty know. Val, being deaf, realised immediately that the only way she could do this was by sending an email and a text message to draw attention to the email. Throughout the following day we exchanged text messages to inform each other of what was happening. Val was able to let Bunty know when she was on the train to York, when she arrived at York, and when she got a taxi so that Bunty was able to meet her at the door of the hotel. Without modern technology Val would have had to rely on other people to let Bunty know what the situation was, which would have meant a loss of independence and privacy. Because of technology, Val did not have to think twice about coping like everybody else.

Relatives and friends of people who were in the area affected by the tsunami in South East Asia at the end of 2004 were able to read the news ticker at the bottom of the screen on Sky News to check if they were safe, because Sky News had given an email address for people to access. Individuals had also been able to send text messages to their family and friends re-assuring them that they were safe.

We have compiled a list of technical developments that we consider have revolutionised access to communication and to the arts. In our list we have taken every care to ensure that we have not been unrealistic concerning what information technology can provide, and in many cases much will depend on your remaining hearing.

It is important to be aware that, although digital radios provide a better signal than analogue radios, it may not always be possible to understand the information, because you are not able to lipread the visible consonants which help give speech its meaning. Your hearing levels may not enable you to receive a good enough signal to understand sound without any visual clues. However, digital radios have the added advantage of providing information on the display about the programme you are listening to. You can know in an instant which person is speaking or singing, providing you with visual clues to aid your understanding.

Technical developments

- *Computers* – desktop, laptop and palm top versions which can be used for sending emails and pictures, and for accessing the internet.
- *Customer Information Systems (CIS)* – visual display screens and high-visibility signage at air terminals, rail and bus stations, e.g. summary main boards near a station entrance with constantly updated displays on each platform, showing the next trains, or the 'Announce' system on buses, which uses visual indicators displaying the name of the approaching stop and when the bus is coming to a halt.
- *Digital cameras* – for taking pictures that can have an explanation printed on them and then be sent to other people.
- *Digital hearing aids* – can be very finely adjusted to suit your individual needs and

can distinguish between different sounds and selectively increase those you need help with.

◆ *Digital radios* – offer interference-free, crystal clear quality sound, ease of tuning, and a line of text indicating which programme the listener is tuned into.

◆ *Digital television* – offers a wider choice of programmes, a better picture and in what many people think is a clearer subtitle font. Subtitles can be accessed by pressing the relevant button on the remote control or through a menu, and, once selected, remain on all the time.

◆ *DVDs* – many have subtitles for deaf and hard of hearing viewers.

◆ *Electronic notetaking* – a method of communication support where the operator uses a computer to provide a précis of what is being said. It normally uses two laptops, one for the operator and one for the user, and is often used for note-taking in an educational setting. The best known system is SpeedText, which uses software produced by the RNID.

◆ *Fax machines* – (short for 'facsimile') are able to transmit an exact copy or reproduction of a document to another person over the telephone line providing they also have a fax machine.

◆ *Induction loop systems* – provided to help people who use a hearing aid or a portable loop listener receive sound more clearly by cutting out background noise.

◆ *Infrared systems* – similar to loop systems. They consist of a transmitter and a listening receiver. They can be used with and without a hearing aid.

◆ *Internet* – an enormous network of millions of computers allowing constant communication throughout the world. It includes: the World Wide Web, electronic mail (email), File Transfer Protocol (FTP), Internet Relay Chat (IRC) and USENET (news service).

◆ *Internet telephony* – new services that enable people to make telephone calls via the internet on their computers or using appropriate handsets.

◆ *Mobile phones* – it is now possible to locate a person using a mobile phone any-where on the globe. All mobile phones are able to send and receive voice and text (SMS) messages. The most recent ones can send and receive still pictures and video clips and act as a mobile office and personal organiser.

◆ *Relay services* – allow a person who is unable to use a normal voice telephone to make a call to a hearing person. The relay service may use either text (for those who use English) or video (for sign language users). The best known is RNID Typetalk which allows textphone users to make telephone calls to people who do not have a textphone.

◆ *STAGETEXT* – a method of communication support which is becoming widely used in the theatre. Captions are produced by a computer and shown on one or more display units installed on or near the stage synchronised with the dialogue, enabling people with a hearing loss to understand what is being said and to enjoy theatre on an equal basis with their hearing peers. The captions also include sound effects and offstage noises. (These are called 'open captions', which means that they are on display all the time, as opposed to closed captions for subtitles on the television or DVDs, which have to be manually accessed by the user.)

◆ *Subtitles* – available for a wide variety of TV programmes, DVDs and videos. In the United States they are known as 'captions', and that term will sometimes be used here as well. Most are displayed in closed format, which means the user has to select them before they can be viewed. Many newspapers, television maga-zines and other programme listings indicate whether a programme is subtitled, but use different symbols. The most common are S and T (standing for 'Teletext'). DVDs will usually indicate on the packaging whether subtitles are available – a common abbreviation on DVDs is SDH (standing for 'Subtitles for Deaf and Hard of Hearing').

> **Tip: How to access subtitles on analogue television**
>
> 1. Turn your television on.
> 2. Select the channel for your chosen programme.
> 3. Find the text button on your remote control, press it to access Teletext, then press 888.
> 4. Subtitles will appear at the bottom of your screen if available. When you turn off your television, the subtitles will automatically be turned off – therefore the above procedure should be followed to access subtitles the next time you watch the television. (Note that the procedure for selecting subtitles on digital TV is not the same. They will be selected either through a menu or by pressing a subtitle button on the remote control. However, once selected, digital subtitles remain on, even when you change channel or turn the television off.)

- *Textphones* – enable those who do not have enough hearing to use a normal voice telephone to make telephone calls. A textphone has a keyboard and a display screen, so that instead of speaking the user types what they want to say, and reads what the other textphone user types in reply on the display. If a textphone user wants to telephone a hearing person, or somebody who does not have a textphone, then they will need to use a relay service. Some textphones have a handset so that a user with a good voice can speak rather than typing. The best known textphones are the Minicom range.
- *Verbatim speech to text reporting* (also known as STT) – a method of communication support where the operator (known as a verbatim reporter or STTR) types using a special keyboard linked to a laptop computer, and the software converts the input into English words displayed on either the laptop screen, external monitor or large screen via a data projector. Because the operator inputs speech phonetically syllable by syllable rather than letter by letter they can provide a verbatim transcript of what is being said. There may be errors in the output if the word is not in the operator's dictionary, in which case it will appear syllabically, e.g. 'bureau' might appear as 'bu ro'. The best known systems are Palantype and Stenograph – the latter is also used for live subtitling on TV.
- *Videos* – with captions. These are fast becoming obsolete because of the growth of DVDs, which give better picture quality and greater flexibility.
- *Video conferencing* – is a vehicle for interactive communication using computers. It enables one set of people to see and hear another set of people in a different location. It brings the world into the classroom, office or conference hall and enables participants to speak directly to their colleagues and experts in other parts of the world.
- *Visual display screens and high-visibility signage* – at air terminals, rail and bus stations.
- *Voice recognition* – software that converts sounds, words or phrases into text, which is then displayed. Also called 'speech recognition'. Most software needs to be trained to recognise the speaker's voice (known as 'speaker dependent'). It is increasingly being used for live subtitling on TV and elsewhere. Speaker-independent voice recognition software is being developed but is not yet reliable.
- *Web conferencing* – is cost effective, time efficient, and expands on basic video

conferencing enabling individuals to communicate 'face-to-face' using their desk or laptop computer, whether they are in the same building or across the world.

Access to information through communication support

Although this chapter has concentrated on how access to information is made possible by the use of technology, there are occasions when that access requires the support of a trained professional rather than an inanimate machine. Communication support is often provided for hard of hearing and deaf people by Language Service Professionals (LSPs), who were previously known as Human Aids to Communication (HACs). There are several types of LSP – sign language interpreters for those who use BSL, lipspeakers, manual and electronic note-takers and verbatim speech to text reporters (STTRs) for those who use speech, and deafblind communicators for those who have a dual sensory disability.

◆ *Lipspeakers* convey a speaker's message without using their voice. They produce the shape of the words with exceptional clarity, reproduce the rhythm and phrasing of natural speech and repeat the stress used by the speaker to enable the message to be passed to the deaf person. Facial expression, natural gesture and finger spelling are also used to aid understanding.
◆ *Manual note-takers* work mainly with deaf students in education, and with deaf and hard of hearing people at work and at conferences and meetings. They take handwritten notes, providing a précis of what is said rather than a verbatim record.
◆ *Electronic note-takers* and *Verbatim speech to text reporters* both use technology to deliver the communication support, and definitions of both will be found in the list of technical developments earlier in this chapter.

An organisation called the Council for the Advancement of Communication with Deaf People (CACDP) is an awarding body for qualifications in this area, and maintains a register of LSPs who have been awarded such a qualification. Using a registered LSP means that the user can be assured they have been properly trained and will give a proper level of professional service. All LSPs have strict codes of practice covering things like confidentiality.

Many LSPs are freelance and can be booked directly, but also work for communication support agencies such as those run by the RNID. Because they are a scarce resource, LSPs can be quite expensive, but the money to pay for them can be obtained under the Access to Work scheme for those who are in employment (see Chapter 15). They would also be considered a reasonable adjustment under the DDA (Disability Discrimination Act 1995) in many circumstances, in which case the person providing the service should meet the cost. Most deaf and hard of hearing organisations use LSPs at their meetings and conferences to ensure that members can follow the proceedings, and you may have seen them at work in television reports on party political conferences and trade union meetings.

John became profoundly deafened as a result of meningitis at the age of 22. For a long time he found it extremely difficult to communicate with family and friends, apart from face-to-face encounters and writing letters. Over the years technological developments materialised, which gave him back his independence, freedom and dignity.

When he was in his early forties he had to attend a conference, after which he was meeting a friend for a meal. They were also going to see a subtitled English speaking film that had recently won an Oscar, which meant he would not have to wait for it to be shown on TV.

He had just started a new job and was looking forward to learning more about the international perspectives of his work, and meeting his new colleagues. He felt quite confident that he would be able to understand the proceedings because he had been able to book a SpeedText operator through Access to Work. He had used the service before, and knew he would be sent a written version of the proceedings to refer to later in case he missed anything.

He also felt relieved; his mother had been unwell and he had been able to have a brief conversation with her using his Minicom before he left for his train and she had told him she was feeling much better. He found it difficult to concentrate when he was worried.

The conference was several miles from his home, so he travelled there by train. He was able to receive a discount because he had a Disabled Persons Railcard. He already knew exactly where the meeting was being held because he had received an email with all the details.

He had also sent a text message, and a picture of himself, to a colleague while he was on the train and received one in return. They had previously arranged to find a quiet place to meet at lunch time to discuss some of their mutual work activities and become better acquainted.

As he had expected, when he arrived at the conference he was given a designated seat with a small computer monitor next to a SpeedText operator. He felt positive because he was going to be able to understand the proceedings.

The conference progressed well. Conversation had been difficult during the coffee break, but he was able to have some discussions with the delegates, provided that he could see their faces. He met his new colleague and they had an interesting discussion about their families because they had managed to find a well-lit corner with few distractions.

After the conference he was extremely tired because he had been lipreading and reading text all day. He was pleased to have time to recover on the train. He had known the friend he was meeting for a long while and could lipread him well. He was not experiencing the overwhelming anxiety he often felt when he met new people whom he was not at all sure he would understand.

He enjoyed the evening, the film was very funny and he was able to laugh when everybody else did because of the subtitles. When he arrived home, he watched the World Snooker Championship, which he had recorded earlier using his new DVD recorder, to help him relax and recover from a long day.

It had been a productive and satisfying day thanks to the new technology.

Chapter 13

The telephone

Nearly everyone knows that the telephone was invented by Alexander Graham Bell. What some people do not know is that both Bell's mother and his wife were deaf. Although Bell invented the telephone, he really wanted to find some device that would make life easier for deaf people. Ironically, he invented something that caused them more communication problems – not fewer!

This chapter does not contain a detailed account of various forms of telecommunication devices. Technology changes so fast nowadays that anything we wrote today could well be out of date by the time you read it. Not only does telephone technology change rapidly, but so does hearing aid technology. There are many different makes and models of hearing aid and implant. You will need to check that any piece of special telephone equipment you select is compatible with your hearing aid or implant. What you will find here are some guidelines and suggestions.

What is the point of equipment?

If it does not:

- enable you to perform a task more easily;
- help you to keep your independence;
- improve the quality of your life;
- give you equal access to leisure, employment and education;
- maintain your equality with hearing people,

it is just an expensive and unnecessary gadget!

What are the problems raised by the use of equipment?

- Non-disabled people may assume that the equipment has solved all your hearing problems and therefore you ought to be able to do everything that they can do!
- Equipment is not always understood, used or installed properly. Someone may be sold a telephone with an induction loop only to discover that their hearing aid does not have a telecoil in it.
- Equipment is not always maintained, e.g. your local theatre may have an infrared system installed, but it may not be working.
- Staff do not always know how to use equipment, e.g. your bank may have a textphone, but none of the staff knows how to answer it.
- Equipment/technology may be so hyped in the media that it gives false hope, e.g. cochlear implants were hailed as 'bionic ears' by many newspapers, which led a lot of deaf and hard of hearing people to think that a cure for deafness had been found. The truth – that implants are useful for a small number of deaf people but are by no means a 'cure', was very disappointing for some.

The point of equipment is not to make life easier for non-disabled people, nor to salve their consciences about us. Equipment should enable us to move from focusing on what we cannot do, to focusing on what we can do. Never let anyone get away with trying to define you by what you cannot do.

You are not Christopher who cannot use the telephone, but Christopher who is an expert at communicating by email or writing eloquent and articulate letters.

Does your heart sink when the telephone rings?

The most important thing to remember about the telephone is that **it is not necessary to use it**.

This is a beautiful and inspiring thought. The telephone is a useful way to communicate, but it is not the only way. If possible you could use:

◆ fax
◆ email
◆ letter
◆ text messaging using a mobile telephone
◆ textphone
◆ videophone
◆ face to face meeting
◆ video conferencing
◆ amplified telephone with loop system.

Even as we write some of these pieces of equipment are becoming out of date. But you get the point, I hope – be creative, use an alternative. Here are some examples of how to do so.

Query
My bank refuses to do business, except over the telephone.

Possible solution
Write a letter to the bank manager (or Head Office, if necessary) explaining your problem. If that does not work, take your business to a bank that will accommodate you. Banks are in business; they cannot afford to lose customers. In any case, do you seriously want to do business with someone who cannot care less about deaf people?

Query
My GP insists that I telephone to make an appointment.

Possible solution
GPs' surgeries are equipped with computers nowadays. Ask to use email facilities instead. Hospitals and GP surgeries are obliged to provide facilities for disabled patients. If you do not have access to email, discuss the problem face to face with the Practice Manager. Together you can come up with a sensible solution that could be used by all hard of hearing and deaf patients in the practice. The bottom line is that you need to be able to reach medical help in an emergency.

In an emergency

You are alone in the house. It is the middle of the night. You have no hearing at all. You are ill and frightened. What do you do?

1. Dial 999.
2. Pause.

3. Say that you are completely deaf and cannot hear anything and need help.
4. Tell them your name, address and telephone number.
5. Tell them your problem.
Repeat 1 to 5 several times.

6. Leave the telephone off the hook.
7. If you can, make sure the chain and bolts are off your front door.
8. Wait.
9. Repeat 1 to 5 until help comes.

It is very sensible to provide for a situation like this by arranging a code with a friend or relative. It is helpful to have someone you can ring in an emergency with whom you can leave a message asking them to telephone 999. Some local authorities provide alarms, which can be worn around the neck and pressed in an emergency so that help will come. Try to leave a key with a neighbour or next of kin. Be sensible: if there was an emergency, how would you cope? Make a few plans now.

Do you want to continue to use the telephone?

Here are some suggestions if you decide that you do.

Exchange your existing telephone

Exchange your existing telephone for a model more suited to your hearing loss, such as an amplified telephone with a loop system (these are available from BT and other suppliers). This has a volume control (so that you can make the other person's voice louder) and a loop system (so that you can cut out any background noise from your end). It also has an extra loud bell and can have a flashing light device added (to alert you to the fact that the telephone is ringing).
Take into consideration:

◆ how much residual hearing you have, if any;
◆ whether your hearing aids/implant have a loop facility;
◆ whether you need to lipread;
◆ whether you prefer to read speech rather than hear it;
◆ how you wish to be alerted – flashing light, loud bell, pager, Hearing Dog;
◆ how much you can afford.

Make the most of your telephone and hearing aids/implants

Before beginning your conversation, make sure that the earpiece of the receiver is held to the microphone on your hearing aid/implant. (If you are not sure where this is, ask your audiologist or Hearing Therapist. The microphone is situated in different places depending on which model hearing aid/implant you have.)
If your telephone has a loop system, switch your hearing aid/implant to the loop (or telecoil) position (usually the 'T' switch) and place the receiver close to the telecoil in your hearing aid. (Ask your audiologist or Hearing Therapist where this is.)

Use a code

Some people with a little residual hearing find this helpful. It only works if the person at the other end of the telephone knows the code too. The idea is that the hard of hearing/deaf person calls their hearing friend and asks a series of closed questions – that is questions that only require the answer 'Yes' or 'No'. The hearing person replies saying either 'Yes, yes' or 'No' depending on the answer. An example of how this works is shown below.

> **Deaf person:** Hello, this is Jane. Remember our Code? Two 'Yes' for 'Yes' and one 'No' for 'No'.
> **Hearing person:**[1] Yes, yes.
> **DP:** Are you still free on Wednesday morning, Martin?
> **HP:** Yes, yes.
> **DP:** Shall we meet at 10.00am?
> **HP:** No.
> **DP:** Shall we meet at 11.00am?
> **HP:** Yes, yes.
> **DP:** Shall we meet at the usual place?
> **HP:** Yes, yes.
> **DP:** My turn to pay for coffee?
> **HP:** No.
> **DP:** See you Wednesday at 11.00am at the High Street Coffee Shop.
> **HP:** Yes, yes.

Some people tap the receiver with a pencil instead of speaking. Twice for 'yes' and once for 'no'.

Use an attachment

Some telephones, especially mobile telephones, can be used with a neck loop or a similar attachment (see RNID Solutions catalogue or Connevans catalogue for details – Appendix 1). Apart from cutting out background noise, some people find that loop systems clarify sound. Remember that some mobile or cordless telephones are not compatible with some models of hearing aids because they cause interference. Check before you buy!

Use your 'better' ear

Quite a lot of hard of hearing and deaf people feel that they can hear better with one of their ears than the other – regardless of what an audiogram may show. If you feel that, then use your better ear to hear with on the telephone. Even a slight difference in hearing may make a great improvement with the telephone.

Repeat back

To check that you have heard correctly, and to avoid confusion, check back any important information received. For example, it is sensible to check things such as times, dates, places, names and figures. This is good business practice anyway! The following conversation shows how this might work.

> **Deaf person:** So, the committee meeting is on Wednesday morning at 10.30am at Hearing Concern Headquarters.
> **Hearing person:** No, it's on Thursday morning.
> **DP:** Thursday morning?
> **HP:** Yes, that's right.

Spell it!

Ask people to spell words that are difficult to hear:

HP: Hello, my name is Carruthers.
DP: Could you spell that please?
HP: C, A, R, R, U, T, H, E, R, S.
DP: Carruthers?
HP: That's right.

Spell it again please!

Ask people to spell words that are hard to hear using the 'A' for apple method.

HP: Our head office is in Silver Street.
DP: Please spell that using the 'A' for apple method.
HP: Sure, that's 'S' for sugar, 'I' for igloo, 'L' for lamp, 'V' for Victor, 'E' for egg and 'R' for rabbit.
DP: Silver Street?
HP: That's right, as in gold and silver, you know?
DP: Of course.

Write and right!

Ask people to put things in writing. This is extremely sensible especially when transacting business, whether you are deaf or hearing.

DP: I'm happy to speak at your conference in July, but please could you put all the details in a letter? I like to have everything on file.
HP: No problem. I'll put it in the post today.

Use an extension and a hearing colleague

The hearing colleague (B) faces you (C) and, using a telephone extension, listens in on your conversation and lipspeaks the other side of the conversation for you. You (C) read your colleague's lips (B) and reply to the person (A) on the other end of the telephone.

A. **Hearing person:** speaks to colleague via extension and listens to deaf person.
B. **Colleague:** listens to hearing person via extension and lipspeaks to deaf person.
C. **Deaf person:** lipreads colleague and speaks to hearing person.

I had worried, for example, about the telephone. It was essential for busy active MPs, and as I was totally deaf it seemed beyond my reach. But checking with the telephone authorities, she found that they could provide an ear-piece extension which enabled her to listen and repeat simultaneously the words of a caller; I lip-read her and answered accordingly. With practice, the system became near word perfect. With the help of Pauline and my secretary I have used the telephone without difficulty over the years, including doing many live national radio interviews.

Jack Ashley, 1994

What are friends for?

Get someone else to make your telephone calls in exchange for helping them. In a busy office, a deaf person might ask a colleague to take a difficult call in exchange for help with drafting a complicated document or doing the filing. Everyone needs help with something – why not make something positive out of that!

Some advantages and disadvantages of the telephone

Advantages

- ◆ Instant reply
- ◆ Friendly
- ◆ Nearly everyone has one.

Disadvantages

- ◆ Cannot lipread over the telephone.
- ◆ Cannot see facial expressions or body language, which provide much-needed clues for deaf people.
- ◆ Accents become more pronounced and therefore more difficult to hear.
- ◆ There are sometimes bips, squeaks and funny noises.
- ◆ Recorded messages, electronic voices and answerphones are a nightmare for some deaf people.
- ◆ People do not always speak into the receiver. Some also speak too fast or mutter, chew, giggle, etc.
- ◆ Background noise – people often call from a busy office with background chatter or from their home with the television on. Infuriatingly, you can often pick up the background noise better than you can hear what they are saying.

What happens if I cannot use a normal telephone at all?

Many of the tips in this chapter will help you if you have some useful residual hearing that allows you to use a normal voice telephone in the ways we have suggested. But if you are profoundly deaf and cannot use a normal telephone at all, even with the help of amplification and a loop, all is not lost – there are solutions available that allow you to maintain your independence and your ability to use the telephone.

In the previous chapter we showed how the authors of this book were able to communicate about a meeting in York by email and texting with their mobile phones, even though Val is unable to use a voice telephone. This is a good example of how a mainstream technology created for the general population – text messaging – has benefited deaf people.

Textphone

However, neither email nor text messaging is real-time – you have to send the message and then wait for the other person to read it and reply. But there is an equivalent to the real time dialogue that hearing people have using the telephone – and that is the textphone. It is not our intention to go into any detail about this technology, but you will find a basic description of what a textphone does in the previous chapter. They can be obtained from specialist suppliers such as the RNID and Connevans (see Appendix 1), but you can also obtain one free from the Social Services if you are profoundly deaf, although there may be a waiting list. A textphone replaces speech by typed text, but many textphones incorporate a handset or speakerphone so you can use voice one way and text the other. Many people are reluctant to use a textphone because they cannot type fast – do not worry about that, as many textphone users have the same problem, and most are one or two finger typists.

Typetalk

What do you do if you want to telephone a hearing friend or a business? Increasingly businesses do have textphones and can take calls from textphone users, but obviously there will be many occasions when you want to telephone somebody who does not have one. This is still possible – in this case you make the call using a relay service for textphone users. The best known in the UK is Typetalk, which is run by the RNID. When a textphone user makes a call to somebody who has only an ordinary telephone a Typetalk operator relays what the textphone user has typed to the hearing person, and then types back what they say in reply to the textphone user. In fact, the textphone user can speak directly to the hearing person, and simply get the typed replies via the Typetalk operator. At first it seems strange to have a third person involved in the call, but all the relay operators are bound by strict codes of confidentiality. Typetalk handles thousands of calls every week, and has given profoundly deaf people the ability to use the telephone just like everyone else. And hearing people can make calls to textphone users in exactly the same way, with the relay operator facilitating the call.

Finally

- ◆ **You do not have to be able to hear to survive.**
- ◆ **You do not have to be able to hear to communicate.**

Notes

1 Of course, the other person could be hard of hearing too! All the more reason for care and courtesy on *both* sides!

Chapter 14

Bridging the generation gap

As we mentioned in the Introduction, we were inspired to write this book because so many of the deaf and hard of hearing people we have met have not properly realised how they can help themselves to understand speech better. There has been little doubt in our minds that the generation gap has been one of the trickiest to bridge. Children with high pitched voices, we have been told, are often out of the hearing range of people who have experienced a noise-induced or age-related hearing loss, both of which make it difficult to discriminate the high pitched consonants that give speech its meaning.

Frustratingly for us, many people believe that they should be able to hear perfectly though a hearing aid or a cochlear implant, and have not realised that, in order to understand speech, eyes and ears have to work together.

Those of you who unfortunately have little or no useful hearing will, we know, have appreciated that, unless you have some visual clues, you will not be able to comprehend speech.

You may be reading this book because you have developed a gradual loss of hearing. This is perfectly normal, and you may be interested to know you are not alone – there are about nine million people who are deaf or hard of hearing in the UK, most of whom have lost their hearing gradually with increasing age. Age-related hearing loss is very common, affecting more than half of those over 70 years old in the UK. It involves a progressive loss of hearing, beginning with the loss of high-frequency sounds such as speech, especially in a noisy environment. It is often accompanied by recruitment, which basically means that sounds become too loud too quickly, something you may have already experienced. Hearing aids are helpful, but, as mentioned in Chapter 5, they are not always as useful as you had hoped.

Many of you may be experiencing difficulties with your vision making it difficult to lipread. Some of you, as mentioned before, may have a long-standing hearing loss and have become accustomed to lipreading and watching for all the visual clues available to you. Maybe you have already read the chapter on lipreading (Chapter 7) and have discovered that you are a more proficient lipreader than you had realised.

You may be anxious because you are blaming yourself for not understanding what people say, and think it is your fault because you are not paying attention properly, or putting enough effort into the situation. Unless you have been advised by your consultant that you have another disorder affecting your ability to hear, which is not related to your ears, then you can assume that it is the environment and other circumstances out of your control that contribute to your misunderstanding. Think about the following – have any of these factors made it difficult for you to understand what is being said?

- *The environment* – bright sunlight shining directly in your eyes; uncarpeted floors; loud background noise; sudden loud announcements; inadequate lighting
- *Speech patterns* – foreign or local accents
- *Speech sound* – high pitched or shrill
- *Facial characteristics* – thin lips
- *Skin colour* – dark skin so that the lips are not so well defined, especially when the light is behind the speaker

◆ *Hair* – long hair falling over the face
◆ *Physical movements* – fidgeting; overexcited activity.

All these factors contribute toward the difficulties of communicating with the younger generation and can affect the spontaneity of the relationship. Yet somehow young children, more so than teenagers, are less embarrassed about devising new and novel ways of communicating – using gestures can be seen as just another way of talking, and they may delight in challenging you to work out what the subject is. It is not patronising – it is fun.

It can provide an opportunity not only to educate young people about the impact of not always understanding the spoken word, but also to discover other ways of communicating, such as writing and sending postcards and letters.

Technology is becoming less expensive and is a common feature on the school curriculum; it can be used to deliver a message of love and care. Children are completely fearless and quickly learn to send emails and text messages, and to operate camera phones and webcams. Unless you are a confirmed 'Luddite' you will be received with joy and be called cool when your young acquaintance realises that you are already familiar with the new technology. They will delight in telling you how to use it, and you in turn will have demonstrated your wisdom in acknowledging that we can learn from those younger than ourselves.

Loving relationships, which are frequently the hallmark of a solid trusting experience across the generations, have the potential to develop into a long-standing friendship, and the memories of the enchanting occasions you have shared will last forever, serving to give pleasure in later years when young people develop their own lives in which you may not participate so regularly.

A loss of hearing can affect the naturalness of the special relationship that you enjoy with the younger members of your life, but as with other communication breakdowns this can be managed. The strategies you are about to learn are the response to a question and answer session following a paper called 'Bridging the communication gap'(1995).

An example of global communication

While she was on holiday in Norway, the middle-aged friend of a 16-year-old, who was on a school trip in China and with whom she had not communicated with for some time, received a text message from her to say she had bought a pair of shoes very cheaply and the weather was very hot. A short message but the contact was there because she had her mobile phone switched on!

Suggestions for bridging the communication gap

Verbal misunderstandings

◆ Before engaging in any communication switch on all the lights, turn off background noise and move to somewhere quiet. If you are at ease with doing this, explain why you need to make the changes.
◆ Sit at the same level – it is easier to lipread and hear better if you are not looking down. Use your hearing aid and wear your glasses.

- Have some colourful writing material handy for both of you to write down any words that have been misunderstood; this can become a learning experience for the child.
- Play board games, which require less verbal interaction.
- Use any personal listening devices you have – young people are sometimes less embarrassed about using them than their older peers.

Education

- Cooking can be fun and informative but do try to avoid chatting at the same time. It is simply too difficult to understand speech when you are both engrossed in weighing ingredients, filling cake cases, beating eggs, heating water, etc.
- When explaining to children about an interesting outdoor feature, choose a broad path where you can walk side by side and are able to lipread without fear of tripping over an obstacle or treading in some dog dirt. If you wear a hearing aid choose a quieter place with a minimum of background noise in which to walk.
- Share a video or TV programme without sound but with subtitles – this may help with spelling.
- Read or tell a story at bedtime.

Travelling

- Short familiar trips are less problematic – when the route is known it avoids the need to read a map or keep checking the route.
- New trips should be arranged ahead, making it into an adventure where the child feels included in the planning and all involved know exactly what is happening.
- Plan some quiet time for all to recuperate at the end of the journey.

Helping children cope with a break-up of a parental relationship

- Send regular postcards to create a sense of continuity.
- Ensure there is a special mug or a brightly coloured duvet or quilt, which belongs solely to the child.
- Bring out the family photographs.
- Have a special cupboard box or drawer for the child.
- Have only one child to visit at a time.
- Share the child's pain and insecurity in a companionable way – just being there helps.

Distant relationships

- Send regular postcards – these help with reading skills; they are something to show friends and the teacher; they start a collection of interesting facts; help share knowledge; and are something to look forward to.
- Use email and text messaging to remain in touch.
- If you have the capital, purchase a mobile phone with a camera that can quickly take a photo and send it around the globe, or a webcam, which will capture still images and videos and enable you to send them to your young companions.

Chapter 15

Work

This chapter will concentrate on strategies that we hope will enable you to cope to the best of your ability at work. You may not be aware of the amount of energy you are expending to keep your position, and you may have felt exhausted interacting with colleagues and wondered why this should be the case.

Lipreading and listening when you have a loss of hearing can be tiring, and it is of vital importance to have frequent eye breaks. Many members of the Association of Teachers of Lipreading to Adults are deaf or hard of hearing, and their meetings always include these.

However, the amount you are able to understand may fluctuate depending on environmental factors, and on your emotional or physical state. People talking over each other may be another hindrance to comprehension. In addition to your hearing loss you may also experience low vision, and will require other support such as large print memos and specially adapted screens for your computer.

Work, whether it be paid or voluntary, is an important aspect of life. In the United Kingdom paid work can account for up to 48 hours a week of a person's life until they reach retirement age, currently 65 for men and 60 for women. (This is due to change in April 2020, when the government raises the state pension age for both men and women to 65.)

There will be many people aged over 50 who, according to REACH (the charity that offers a free UK-wide job-finding service to volunteers with management and professional experience and skills), will have 'Abundant energy and enthusiasm which, combined with their qualifications, skills and life experience, makes them a huge asset to any voluntary organisation.' REACH also point out that 'Volunteers can choose the work pattern which suits their lifestyle, keep their career skills alive and enjoy being part of a working team doing something worthwhile. In voluntary work people are interested in what you can do – not how old you are.'

It would therefore seem that the world of work does not always finish when you retire, and, whatever sort of work you do, understanding often essential information is central to job satisfaction and the ability to perform a task. Whether you have a profound or mild hearing loss your hearing may let you down, and it is important to be realistic about how this affects your ability to function effectively in the workplace.

Fortunately legislation such as the DDA (Disability Discrimination Act 1995) makes it unlawful for your employer to discriminate against you, and you have a right to ask for some reasonable adjustments to be made. These could include:

◆ being given time off to attend a lipreading class or a session with a Hearing Therapist;
◆ allocating some of the duties you are unable to undertake personally, such as using the telephone;
◆ arranging for you to have special equipment such as a radio aid or a telephone with an amplified handset and an inductive coupler;
◆ providing support such as a lipspeaker or note-taker at meetings and interviews;
◆ arranging an internal transfer to a post more suitable for you.

Another programme available is Access to Work. Under this scheme you can apply for communication support when being interviewed for a job. If you are successful in your application, your employer can then request financial assistance of up to 100% of approved costs to help with any problems that are likely to occur as a result of your hearing loss. If you are already working, then your employer can apply for a proportion of approved costs to provide you with whatever aid to communication is most beneficial for you. You can apply for Access to Work under the government funding scheme run by Jobcentre Plus. It is available to you whether you are unemployed, employed or self-employed, and can apply to any job, full-time or part-time, permanent or temporary. This assistance is for a maximum period of 3 years, after which the Access to Work Business Centre will review your support and the circumstances. Access to Work may provide help for a further period if your employer continues to be eligible for help under the rules that then apply.

A colleague of ours, who is profoundly deaf, is able to have the support of a lipspeaker at meetings – her employer can claim for this through Access to Work. Another person we know, who has lost most of his useful hearing and wears two powerful hearing aids, has received a radio aid through Access to Work, which has been a 'life-enhancer' for him.

Perhaps it is reassuring to know that support is available, but whatever type of work you are doing or would like to do it is important to be realistic about your selection. If the job involves telephoning customers or relying on your hearing to understand precise instructions from a distance or in a noisy environment, then the job may not be for you. However, you could always be responsible for managing personnel who are able to undertake these tasks. It is important to remain positive about what you can do, and use your previous training, background and skills to achieve this. Work out what changes you can make to enable you to feel confident that you have done your best to take responsibility for any adjustments you require as a result of your inability to hear. Not understanding speech as clearly as a hearing person does not mean you cannot function in the workplace. So whether you are gainfully employed or have a desire to voluntarily put something back into the community, there are several challenges to be faced such as interviews, the job itself (especially if your hearing loss occurs whilst you are working), networking and socialising.

Tip

If you are really experiencing difficulty telling people you have a hearing loss, why not practise telling a shop assistant that you have a problem with your hearing and have to lipread, and see what their reaction is. It may not be as negative as you had feared and they will try to be helpful. If they seem annoyed, try not to take offence – they may be having a bad day too and it is nothing to do with you.

Interviews

- ◆ Prepare yourself thoroughly making notes of all proper names and the aims of the organisation.
- ◆ Always advise the interviewers about your hearing loss in advance. Make your position clear in a positive manner. If you require communication support, such as a lipspeaker, request this as soon as you know the date of the interview and at the same time advise the panel that you will be using some communication support. It may well be a new experience for them and by being honest about your needs you may help to increase the understanding of those present, which will result in a smoother interview.
- ◆ Allow plenty of time for travelling and arrive 10 minutes early – no sooner or you might find yourself becoming unnecessarily anxious.
- ◆ Arrange things to your satisfaction, ensuring you are not sitting near a partly open window and that traffic noise is not disturbing you. Sit so that you can see the interviewers' faces clearly – the initiative has to come from you.
- ◆ If you are not sure you have understood a question, ask for it to be written down – preferably on your own pad as you may wish to refer to this later.
- ◆ Respond positively to questions, and appear confident by saying how you would undertake some of the tasks the job requires.
- ◆ If the subject of using the telephone comes up, be positive and say which piece of equipment would be helpful and how it can be obtained.

Developing a hearing loss whilst at work

Accept and acknowledge that you are experiencing difficulties, and do so in a way that you feel most comfortable with. This may take some courage, because you are worried that it is an admission of failure on your part and that others may not understand. It is better to admit you do not always know when a person is speaking because of your hearing loss, rather than be seen as stupid, rude or stuck-up. A loss of hearing is invisible and nobody looks deaf! Here are some suggestions to help you:

- ◆ Let your employer know that you are experiencing difficulties and explain how it might affect your job.
- ◆ Speak to your human resources manager (if you have one) or your line manager about your problem. They may be able to advise you about a helpful approach, or may even be willing to explain the position on your behalf if you give them permission to do this.
- ◆ Find out what equipment is available to help you cope better.
- ◆ Advise your employer of any changes that might enhance your ability to carry out your work, e.g. changing the position of your desk so that it is facing your colleagues and allows you to see when someone approaches, asking for a written record of all important information.
- ◆ Find a way to open up a discussion with your boss about how you can usefully be employed/deployed. It may help to talk it through first with a person you trust and who has known you for a long time, values your contributions and appreciates your concerns. You could practise what you want to say with them (we call it having a script).
- ◆ Suggest Deaf Awareness sessions are included in staff training days. Mention it could add value to colleagues' lives, both at and outside of work.

Socialising

Not an easy subject, especially if you have experienced some very difficult interactions in the course of your work when you have misunderstood one word and felt sure you have made a total mess of things – or did you?

Look at this:

'Have you got a pen and paper handy?'
'Have you got a paper hanky?'

In poor light and background noise they look and sound similar! Lipreading is not a perfect art and, if you passed a hanky instead of a pen and paper, don't be hard on yourself.

Socialising may be easier if you use small talk and ask to see the person later for a longer conversation in a more favourable environment, or exchange email addresses and business cards. You may find the following suggestions helpful when you are at a social gathering.

- Smile – think of any social occasion as an opportunity, not a nightmare.
- Brief yourself – have something of interest from the news to talk about to fellow guests.
- Think of sentences starting How … Why … Where … When … What …
- Ask people about themselves – they'll be happy to tell you.
- Be complimentary where you can – people will respond.
- Keep a list of simple opening lines: 'How long have you worked here?'; 'Where do you live?'; 'Have you been on holiday recently?'; 'How do you know our host?'
- Use a neutral subject like the weather to start a conversation – how the other person responds is often a good indication about how they are feeling and whether they wish to continue the conversation. It also offers an opportunity for you to see if you can understand them.
- Be prepared for people talking over each other – try to move one person away from the group and speak to them individually.
- Carry a supply of cards with your details on them.
- Keep a pen and pad handy for people to write down their name – in our multicultural society many names are unfamiliar and difficult to lipread.

It is important to accept the challenge of socialising to lessen the possibility of becoming isolated. Be aware that, although you may have a real desire to understand everything, this can be a barrier to progress because it can provoke feelings of failure and helplessness. It is much better to be glad about what you can understand and adjust your expectations, otherwise you may become exhausted because you have concentrated so hard – remember your eyes are your ears.

Making an effort will have the following positive outcomes:

- Meeting colleagues on neutral territory and talking about your own and other's problems away from work.
- Providing an opportunity to gain support for your communication needs.
- Letting colleagues know about any sport you enjoy and what hobbies you are interested in.
- Becoming more aware of work politics and other general issues.
- Gaining an opportunity for colleagues to ask you more about yourself.
- Showing that you are interested in colleagues' lives and are keen to get on with them.

- Improving your quality of life at work by knowing people better.
- Feeling part of things.

Not making an effort can result in a vicious circle (see figure).

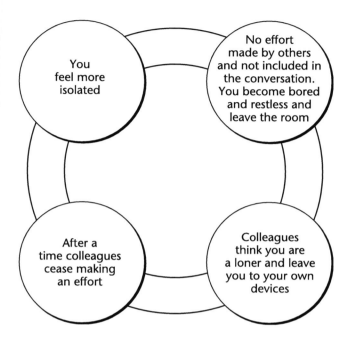

Meetings

Despite the advances of new technology such as video and web conferencing, meetings are still an important feature of most types of work. With careful preparation and knowing your rights you should be able to participate on equal terms.

General approach

- Be open and realistic and have faith in yourself that you can do things.
- Do not apologise for being hard of hearing.
- Explain your difficulty and request eye breaks during the meeting.
- Plan ahead.
- Request any communication support you may need such as note-takers, lipspeakers and Speech to Text Reporters (STTRs).
- Inform your colleagues of your needs.
- Ask for presentation to have captions.
- Request that any questions put to the chair of the meeting are repeated by them.
- Have a sense of humour.
- Self-confidence is necessary but not easy.
- Use lipreading.
- Thank people for their co-operation.

Running a meeting

- Provide a detailed agenda.
- Ask for written contributions or summaries.
- Choose the room and setting carefully (lighting, acoustics, background noise).

- If you feel comfortable, explain you will be running the meeting in a certain way to assist in hearing everything and everyone clearly.
- 'Control' speakers so one person speaks at a time and they do not speak over each other.
- Ask people to indicate before they speak.
- Have speech to text support or use a loop system.
- Sit next to the minute-taker for reference notes.

Attending a meeting

- Ask beforehand for notes or summaries.
- Get there first and choose the best seat for you to follow the meeting.
- Sit in a position not too far away from the main speaker if there is one.
- Position yourself away from distractions, e.g. do not sit with your back to the door.
- Close the window if possible.
- Open the curtains or blinds if possible, unless this would mean the sun is in your eyes.
- Reorganise the furniture.
- Inform the chair person how they can help.
- Ask them to slow down if they read a document, because most people read more quickly than they speak.
- Discuss the problem with as many people as possible.
- Remind people if necessary.
- Ask people to get your attention before they address you.
- Check if a loop system or communication support will be available.
- Take a loop or any equipment you find helpful to smaller meetings/groups.

Chapter 16

Difficult situations

> Maybe the best idea would be to pack a small bag with books and Hershey [chocolate] bars and go away to an isolated cottage somewhere in the wilds. Peacefully alone over Christmas. ... 'No straining to hear above a hubbub of voices. No explaining, 'I have a hearing loss – would you mind saying that again, please? And again? Just one more time, in different words?' No resentment over yet again being the 'odd man out' in a holiday group of chatting people. What good was 'Hark the Herald Angels Sing' when you couldn't hark to them yourself?
>
> Karen Mango, 'Christmas Cheer', in Jepson (ed.), 1997

General principles

For some hard of hearing and deaf people, every situation is a difficult situation! There are hardly any areas of their lives that are not touched by their hearing loss. Whether they are at work, relaxing with their families, or attending an evening class, their lives are different because of their lack of hearing.

Consider how the day begins. The alarm clock sounds. A person with good hearing picks up the alarm clock and switches it off. A hard of hearing person cannot hear the alarm clock for the simple reason that he/she does not wear his hearing aids to sleep in! (There may be a vibrating alarm clock or one with a flashing light.) If a hearing person sleeps through the noise of the alarm clock, the sounds of other people beginning the day – doors slamming, footsteps on the stairs, traffic in the street – will eventually wake them. Deaf people are oblivious to all that.

Some families carry on a conversation while showering, dressing and breakfasting. If you are hard of hearing, conversation is impossible until you have showered, dressed and put in your hearing aids (and put on your glasses too, if they are necessary for lipreading).

Many hearing people will catch up with the day's news by listening to the radio or watching the television while they breakfast. This is not always possible for those who are hard of hearing. Television can be enjoyed by many deaf people only by means of a loop system, infrared device or subtitles. The gadgets are too much of a fiddle in the morning when you are in a hurry, and it is impossible to eat cornflakes and read subtitles at the same time without having to change your shirt.

One of our patients said that her family knows that it is not possible to communicate with her in the mornings until she is going out of the door with her briefcase in her hand! This is because she does not put her hearing aids in until she is ready to leave the house. Why not? She likes to have a shower every morning and wash her hair. Her hair is dried and styled just before she leaves the house. Her hearing aids cannot be put in until after this is done because water, shampoo, hairdryers and hairspray can damage hearing aids. The consequence is that all-important information – such as 'Will you pick the children up from school?' – must be conveyed very carefully in the right way and at the right time, written down or discussed the night before.

This may sound amusing or even faintly bizarre if you are a hearing person and have not encountered deafness before, but consider that tomorrow morning you will be able to hear the alarm clock, the deaf person will not. We have to go through this every morning, and not just every morning but all through the day every day of our lives. We can never cease to be deaf.

So, how does one cope in a difficult situation?

General guidelines

- *Try not to panic.* In the immortal words of Corporal Jones 'Don't panic!' Unfortunately, stress tends to lessen our ability to hear, and our inability to hear increases our stress.

Panic → hear less → more panic → hear even less.

- *Relax.* Learn some simple relaxation techniques to lessen your panic. It is much easier to hear when you are relaxed. Remember that even hearing people cannot hear everything. Some deaf people tend to assume that all hearing people can hear everything that is said to them, but they cannot. It is not at all unusual for anybody to mishear or not hear something.
- *Use your eyes* to help your ears by watching the faces of people who are speaking. You can glean a lot just from their facial expressions, let alone from lipreading. Do you have your glasses on? Can you see the face of the speaker? Is the light on? Is the light on the speaker's face? Ask them to move if it is not.
- *Make the most of your hearing.* Sit, or stand, near the speaker. Sit in the front row at a meeting rather than the back. Put your hearing aid(s) in. Use the loop system if there is one.
- *Plan ahead.* Write and ask what facilities are available, e.g. a loop system or a lipspeaker, and request these if they are not already provided.
- *Be assertive.* A polite request uttered in a pleasant manner and with a smile may help you get what you want. Try to be assertive rather than aggressive. Be prepared to educate people and to provide information about what you require. 'I need a lipspeaker. You can book one by contacting this agency.' 'Communication tactics are really helpful. Here is an information sheet suggesting a few simple things that you can do to help.' Positive suggestions are always more welcome than negative complaints.

Do not say: 'I can't hear you.'

but

'I can't hear you because I can't see your face. I am hard of hearing and I need to see your face clearly to be able to lipread. Thank you.'

Philosophy

Sometimes, despite your best efforts, you will meet people who are rude, selfish, uncaring and downright unpleasant. Life is like that. Remember they have the problem not you. **You cannot help being deaf, but they can help being disagreeable.**

What follows are not commandments, but guidelines for difficult situations. They will give you some ideas and stimulate you into having ideas of your own. The great thing is not to avoid difficult situations, but to work out how to cope in them, and even enjoy yourself! Remember the woman in the quotation at the beginning of the chapter who was dreading Christmas? Well, here is what happened to her at the carol service.

> Over the past years I have been going for the family company and the beauty of the scene. Forget the service, forget the minister speaking, forget the carols.
>
> Well, this year it was still forget the first two items (and now I thought, common sense uppermost at last, how about getting a loop installed?) but surely carols are meant to be sung! The music distorted and cacophonous to my damaged ears, was still familiar inside my head. I sang along, inaudible to myself, but no heads turned. I went on singing happily.
>
> (Karen Mango, 'Christmas Cheer', in Jepson (ed.), 1997)

In a restaurant

- ◆ Choose a restaurant that uses tablecloths. These help to deaden background noise.
- ◆ Reserve a corner table so that the acoustics are good. (Not one near the kitchen or lavatories!)
- ◆ Ask them to turn down (or off) the background music. Do explain why this is a problem.[1]
- ◆ Sit where you can see most people at the table.
- ◆ Make sure your family or friends know some basic communication techniques before you go out together!

At work

- ◆ Ask the Access to Work team (see Chapter 15) to assess your work situation, to suggest and provide:
  - ▸ suitable equipment, e.g. an amplified telephone;
  - ▸ communication support, e.g. a lipspeaker or note-taker, for important meetings;
  - ▸ Deaf Awareness Training for colleagues.
- ◆ Help yourself by:
  - ▸ arranging assertiveness training – to help you fight for your needs;
  - ▸ making the utmost use of existing resources, e.g. using email instead of the telephone;
  - ▸ suggesting a possible solution whenever you present management with a problem arising out of your hearing loss;
  - ▸ being aware of your rights under the Disability Discrimination Act;
  - ▸ speaking to your union representative;
  - ▸ putting up a handout on communication tactics where your colleagues can read it![2]

GP/Hospital waiting room

This can be a nightmare for deaf people. Why?

- ◆ *Background noise.* Waiting areas can be very noisy places with telephones ringing, people talking, children crying and staff bustling to and fro. Most hard of hearing people find listening in background noise a problem. Hearing aids tend to pick up and amplify all sound, not just the sounds you want to hear!

- ◆ *Acoustics.* Many clinics tend to be acoustically trying. They are full of hard surfaces, which of course are hygienic because they are easy to clean, but not good from an acoustic point of view. Sound bounces and echoes off these surfaces causing it to become distorted.
- ◆ *Lipreading.* If you are not facing the speaker, it is difficult to lipread them. If they are sitting behind a computer screen when they call out your name, it can be impossible to understand what they are saying.
- ◆ *Unfamiliar voices.* It is more difficult to hear, or lipread, a person you have never met before.
- ◆ *Stress.* Hospitals and surgeries can be stressful places.
- ◆ *Feeling ill.* This is so obvious that staff ought not to need to be reminded of this! People who are sitting in doctors' waiting rooms tend to be feeling ill. People who are feeling ill are not at their best – they may be less good tempered than usual or more tired. They may be less able to concentrate. The problem becomes exacerbated when someone is hard of hearing as well!

The most user-friendly waiting rooms are those that have some method of calling the patient that includes a visual display. A reception desk that has a loop system is also extremely useful. So what can you do to prepare for such an occasion?

- ◆ Take handouts on communication tactics for the staff.
- ◆ Provide some Sympathetic Hearing Scheme stickers for your medical notes.[3] This will alert the staff to the fact that you are a deaf or hard of hearing person every time you visit.
- ◆ Take a symbol of the ear clipped to a passport-sized photograph of yourself which has your name clearly written on the back. Give the card and photograph to the receptionist and explain that you are deaf or hard of hearing and that you will need a member of staff to come and fetch you instead of calling out your name. The card is to remind staff that you are deaf or hard of hearing and the photograph is to enable them to identify you in a crowded waiting room. Unlike a wheelchair or a guide dog, most hearing aids are difficult to spot. Remember to collect the card and photograph when you leave so that you can use them on a subsequent occasion. Be prepared for the fact that you will have to do this every time you go. Receptionists are busy people and do not always remember which patients are deaf or hard of hearing.
- ◆ Take a notebook and pen and ask the doctor to write anything down that you have been unable to hear or lipread. A member of a lipreading class suggested that the doctor would object to this as it would take too long. We timed writing down 'You have laryngitis.' It took fourteen seconds. (Think how much time is wasted when a patient has to make a repeat visit to the doctor because they have not understood what he/she said in the first place!)

Shopping

Think of a list of things that might be said to you when you are shopping. Rehearse the examples below beforehand with a friend or relative (or using a mirror).

'That will be £9.99.'
'Do you have the exact money?'
'How would you like to pay?'
'Do you want cashback?'
'Do you want to keep the hanger?'
'Do you mind change; I've run out of notes?'
'Lovely day isn't it?'

Think of what you could do if you did not understand the other person. For example, take the phrase 'That will be £9.99'. Numbers are notoriously difficult to hear and to lipread. Let's explore some options together.

◆ *Cheat!* Look at the figures on the till. Well, why not?
◆ Ask the assistant to *write the figure down* for you.
◆ *Ask a closed question*, not 'Did you say £9.99 or £5.99?' That is an open question. The person will probably reply by repeating what they said before and so you will be none the wiser. Instead ask, 'Did you say £5.99?' This is a closed question. The person will probably reply by saying either: 'Yes, I said £5.99' or 'No, I said £9.99.' The clue is the Yes or No, not the amount of money.
◆ *Use the loop system*, if there is one. Many banks, post offices and stations have them.
◆ *Body language.* Everyone, hearing and hard of hearing people, uses body language. Repeat the figure you thought you heard and use your fingers to confirm this. People copy body language. The shop assistant will often respond by holding up the correct number of fingers.

Shop assistant: That will be £9.99 please.
Hard of hearing customer: £5.99? (Holds up five fingers once and nine fingers twice.)
Shop assistant: (Shakes head.) No, £9.99. (Holds up nine fingers three times.)

You may find that when you tell people you are deaf or hard of hearing, you will be asked questions about your hearing loss or related matters. Some people find it intrusive and impertinent when complete strangers feel the need to ask you exactly how you went deaf, while others look on it as educative. The more hearing people know about what it is like to have a hearing loss, the better for the rest of us. **Think of yourself as an ambassador or an expert!**

Notes
1 See Dempster, Derek & Josephine (eds), 2004
2 Some excellent handouts on communication tactics are available from the RNID (see Appendix 1).
3 Available from Hearing Concern (see Appendix 1).
4 See Dempster, Derek & Josephine (eds), 2004
5 Contact your local Job Centre for details of this scheme or look on the Access To Work website: http://www.jobcentreplus.gov.uk/cms.asp?Page=/Home/Customers/HelpForDisabledPeople/AccesstoWork
6 Some excellent handouts on communication tactics are available from the RNID (see Appendix 1).
7 Available from Hearing Concern (see Appendix 1).

Suggestions handout

- Try not to panic.
- Relax.
- Use your eyes to help your ears.
- Make the most of your hearing.
- Plan ahead.
- Be assertive.
- Be philosophical.
- Get expert help, e.g. Access to Work.
- Use a notebook and pen.
- Wear a badge.
- Be ingenious and think laterally.

In a restaurant

- Choose a well-lit restaurant that uses tablecloths.
- Reserve a corner table so that the acoustics are good.
- Ask them to turn down (or off) the background music.[4]
- Sit where you can see most people at the table.
- Make sure your family or friends know some basic communication techniques before you go out together!

At work

- Ask the Access To Work[5] Team to assess your work situation to suggest, and provide:
  - suitable equipment;
  - Communicator Support;
  - Deaf Awareness Training for colleagues.
- Help yourself by:
  - arranging assertiveness training;
  - making the utmost use of existing resources;
  - suggesting a possible solution whenever you present management with a problem arising out of your hearing loss;
  - being aware of your rights under the Disability Discrimination Act;
  - speaking to your Union representative;
  - putting up the handout on communication tactics where your colleagues can read it!

GP/Hospital waiting room

- Take handouts on communication tactics for the staff.[6]
- Provide some Sympathetic Hearing Scheme stickers for your medical notes.[7] This will alert the staff every time you visit to the fact that you are a HOH person.
- Take a notebook and pen and ask the doctor to write anything down that you have been unable to hear.
- Take a card with a symbol of the ear on it and clipped to a passport-sized photograph of yourself, which has your name clearly written on the back.
- Give the SHC and photograph to the receptionist and explain that you are HOH and that you will need a member of staff to come and fetch you.
- Remember to collect the card and photograph when you leave so that you can use them on a subsequent occasion.
- Be prepared for the fact that you will have to do this every time you go. Receptionists are busy people and do not always remember which patients are hard of hearing.

Shopping

- ◆ Think of a list of things that might be said to you when you are shopping and rehearse these beforehand with a friend or relative (or a mirror).
- ◆ Think of what you could do if you did not understand the other person. Take for example the phrase, 'That will be £9.99.'
- ◆ Cheat! Look at the figures on the till. Well, why not?
- ◆ Ask the assistant to write the figure down for you.
- ◆ Ask a closed question.
- ◆ Use the loop system, if there is one. Many banks, post offices and stations have them.
- ◆ Repeat the figure you thought you heard and use your fingers to confirm this. The shop assistant will often respond by holding up the correct number of fingers.

Chapter 17

Access to education

This chapter is aimed at reducing the physical and emotional energy required to ensure that your experiences with communication in the learning environment are as positive as possible. Something negative might have happened to you while you were at school, college or university, or whilst you were undertaking some training for your job or attending a course to become better informed about your hobby, and this has made you less confident about your ability to access education. As with so many aspects of living with a hearing loss, the crucial issue is to plan ahead, know your rights and be armed with suggestions that will help with your communication needs.

> The Disability Discrimination Act 1995, Part 4, has a Code of Practice for providers of post-16 education and related services for disabled people and students. It is unlawful to discriminate against you by treating you less favourably than others. It is the duty of responsible bodies to make adjustments, involving the provision of auxiliary aids and services.

First of all, here are two stories.

One of the students on a course for Technical/Rehabilitation Officers that one of us was responsible for organising at the City Lit in London was profoundly deafened, and at one point she said: 'I'm not deaf on Wednesdays'. She went on to explain that, because of the support she was receiving from a note-taker, she felt part of the group and was able to learn at their pace. She was able to concentrate on lipreading the teacher, knowing she would receive a copy of the notes later for reference.

Two years previously, during a tutorial in a tiny room occupied by the head of department, another student had burst into tears, and explained that she had been partially hearing most of her life. She had trained to be a nurse and throughout this time had really struggled with trying to learn. She had continuously asked the teachers to stop pacing up and down and face her in the classroom. Eventually she had reverted to asking other students to take notes for her. In practical sessions she had become very distressed when doctors and nurses spoke to her wearing a mask. She passed her training but the job became too difficult and she had to give up. She then applied to become a Hearing Therapist and in the classroom she was able to participate on equal terms. The City Lit has an equal access to education policy, and she was provided with a note-taker and a loop system. The microphone was used by the other students when they spoke, and she in turn was able to contribute, confident that she had heard correctly and was not excluded from learning.

Both of these students had a positive learning experience, and their lives were transformed because of the choice of support available to them. Observing these equal opportunity practices had also added value to the other students' awareness of the changes they needed to make in how they communicated to enable their peers with a hearing loss to have equal access. They also gained confidence in their own communication skills.

In a paper presented at a conference entitled 'Adjustment to Acquired Hearing Loss', which took place at the University of Bristol Centre for Deaf Studies in 1987, a presentation was given about 'Educational help for hard of hearing and deafened adults'. The presenter considered that it was the social and emotional aspects of learning that were important, and that students should be given every opportunity to contribute to the discussion, and their value should be seen as quite independent of their hearing loss. He concluded that it was important that the reorganisation of what he termed the disturbed 'person–environment systems' came not only from the hearing impaired person but also from hearing people in the environment. This sentiment was echoed at the Third International Conference for Hard of Hearing people in Montreux, Switzerland, where the motto was 'Everyone should understand everything'. The organisers were a mixture of deaf and hard of hearing people. Papers were presented in English, the language of the host country, and up to three other languages. All were transcribed by speech to text reporters and shown on a screen. Access to the information was also available (if it had been requested) via sign language interpreters, lipspeakers and note-takers. Infrared and inductive listening systems were also available. It was major feat of organisation!

One of the authors has regularly attended these conferences, which are held every four years, and the access to these largely educational events has been consistently first class. It was while she was checking the content of a presentation about 'Equal access to education' that she was giving at the Sixth International Conference in Sydney that she heard the presenter of an international piano competition declare on the radio: 'Students make teachers just as much as teachers make students.' It totally fitted her experience since, without the knowledge she has gained from the many deaf and hard of hearing students whom she has had the privilege to teach, she would not have gained the information required to write about the changes that teachers and trainers need to make to ensure that their students have a satisfying learning experience.

A suggested approach

When you know which college or university course you will be attending, arrange a meeting with the Student Support Department. You will be referred to a Disability Adviser or the Learning Support Co-ordinator for help with all aspects of teaching and learning, including lectures, practical sessions, field trips and placements. They will advise you about the Disabled Students Allowance (DSA), which is a basic allowance for large items of equipment and for non-medical personal help. It is not income-assessed.

If it is a work-related training course, advise your boss about Access to Work, which provides financial aid for any support that you may need to enhance your learning (see Chapter 15).

You will be entitled to one of the following options:

◆ sign language interpreter
◆ lipspeaker
◆ note-taker
◆ speech-to-text reporter
◆ loop system
◆ radio aid
◆ adapted computer screen.

The guidelines below are repeated in Appendices 5 and 6 for ease of photocopying.

Suggestions for discussion with tutors

When you meet your tutor or trainer advise them how they can be most supportive of your needs. The following list may be helpful for you to use as guide:

- Discuss the Disabled Students Allowance (DSA) and check what financial support you are entitled to.
- Discuss the Access to Work scheme, if you are on a work-related training course.
- Ask for written information to be available before the start of the course to avoid any misunderstandings.
- Request information in black on yellow or white if you have a visual impairment – it provides greater visual contrast and is easier to read.
- If you are dyslexic Comic Sans MS font may be easier to read, since it is clear and simple, and **a** and **g** look like their handwritten equivalents.
- Ask about visual warning systems such as fire alarms.
- Ask if classrooms are clearly signposted to avoid having to ask someone the way.
- Ask if other students will have name labels; if not, ask for a list of the names to be prepared, which you can use when you are introduced to a new person. You may find it useful to ask them to point out their name on the list.
- Ask if seating can be arranged in a half circle to facilitate lipreading. If this is not possible explain that you would like the teacher to repeat or write questions on the board and explain why.
- If you are using a radio aid explain how it can be best used.
- Check if the videos and DVDs will have captions; if not request an outline of their content.
- Suggest individual tutorials are held in a quiet room with plenty of light.
- Ask if a text or mobile phone number will be available for you to leave a message if you are unable to attend a lecture.
- Discuss ways that you can be helped generally and give the 'Guidelines for tutors' handout to the person who will be teaching you.
- Thank the person for their support.

Guidelines for tutors teaching students with a hearing loss

- Attract the students' attention before you start to speak.
- When talking to the students, speak in a clear, slightly louder than normal, voice – clarity is more important than volume. Speak at a moderate pace.
- Face the students when speaking. Your expression and lip movements will assist in understanding what you are saying.
- Avoid covering your face when you speak.
- When talking, do not turn your head or move around the room or distract the students' attention by making unnecessary hand movements.
- Avoid talking to students with your back to the light.
- Do not talk when your back is towards the class.
- Let your face tell a story.
- Remember to pause to give the students time to absorb information before carrying straight on.
- Use as many visual aids as possible. This will reinforce the students' learning through a medium other than the spoken word. Give them time to take in the content of the visual aid before speaking about it.
- Ensure all DVD and video recordings are shown with captions.
- Give students a printed version of a PowerPoint presentation.

- Make sure that a note pad is available to write down anything that is not understood.
- If possible, avoid wearing glasses that have lens that darken in bright light or are reflective. The students gain a lot from eye contact.
- Avoid wearing large or dangling earrings.
- Students could experience problems lipreading people with a beard or moustache – therefore, if possible, please trim your beard and/or moustache.
- If support workers are present ensure that you have a short break every 20 minutes.
- If practical, locate a small well-lit room for individual tutorials. It will be helpful for lipreading if chairs are at the same level.
- Obtain students' email addresses or mobile phone numbers in the event of a change of teaching arrangements.

Remember that lipreading is tiring.

Chapter 18

Personal space

With more rest we do less but achieve more.

A loss of hearing means that, in order for people to interpret speech and react appropriately, all available visual and acoustic clues have to be used.

If you lost some, most, or all of your useful hearing after being able to hear well, realising that you could no longer just listen and overhear conversation when you chose almost certainly came as a shock, and the added energy required to follow conversation probably left you feeling extremely tired.

There is a reason for this. Scientists have discovered that we have two upper brains rather than one, and they deal with different types of mental activity. The right cortex of the brain deals with rhythm, spatial awareness, Gestalt (the whole picture), imagination, daydreaming, colour and dimension. None of these completely relies on sound to provide information. The left cortex of the brain in most people deals with words, logic, numbers, sequence, linearity, analysis and lists. When the left cortex is dominant the right cortex is resting. Perhaps you have realised that, when you have been engaged in any of the mental activities involving the left-hand side of the brain, you have felt quite exhausted and in need of a rest, whereas doing any activity that requires the use of the right-hand side of the brain leaves you refreshed, and ready to resume an activity that requires more deliberation.

For example, you may have been really concentrating on trying to understand what is being said by a family member or friend, or at the theatre or cinema, in a meeting or a group, and afterwards have felt completely washed-out and longing for some personal space in which to gather yourself and recharge your energy. Taking time out for yourself will help decrease stress and alleviate anxieties.

Some suggestions to create personal space

- ◆ Have frequent eye breaks. Re-focus your eyes by looking at a distant object.
- ◆ Give yourself permission to stop paying attention. Switch off your hearing aid.
- ◆ Determine how much area in a shared space will be devoted to your personal needs and belongings.
- ◆ Create a space of your own where you can control access, albeit in the garden shed or the loft.
- ◆ Establish a feeling of ownership by having your own personal objects, such as a significant photograph or a favourite plant.
- ◆ Encourage others to respect these boundaries.
- ◆ Minimise clutter. If you are surrounded by stuff that you never use, throw it out. Keep only those things that you are happy having around.
- ◆ Schedule withdrawal breaks in your day. Take a walk or sit quietly.
- ◆ Limit interruptions.
- ◆ Plan a regular date to have lunch with a colleague or friend, and take responsibility for choosing the time and venue.
- ◆ Spend time on your own at lunch time – make an excuse or state clearly why you need to be on your own.
- ◆ Imitate Winston Churchill and have a five minute nap.

Chapter 19

Pleasure and hobbies

You may have discovered that, as a result of your hearing loss, some of the social occasions you used to look forward to do not satisfy you any more. They are perhaps a time for you to catch up with peoples' lives, happy or sad. The run-up to these events may progress well, with all the arrangements being made by post, email, SMS and amplified phones with inductive couplers. However, it may be the actual event, the face-to-face interaction, that makes you feel apprehensive.

In the same vein, the hobbies and interests that you once enjoyed are now beyond your ability, because you are unable to understand what members of your local club are saying; or appreciate and enjoy your favourite music; or attend a class to learn more about your hobby; or walk and lipread at the same time; or have a meal with people, because it is difficult to watch what you are eating and lipread at the same time. You can probably identify lots of other areas where you are experiencing problems.

You are not alone. Many people we have met have expressed similar concerns and we appreciate that the journey along the sometimes solitary road to accepting the changes imposed by a loss of hearing cannot be underestimated.

For many people, experiencing a hearing loss has been the catalyst that has prompted them to become more familiar with using email, text messaging and setting the video recorder to record subtitles. Others have suddenly or slowly, depending on the onset of their loss of hearing, realised that it is no longer possible to watch a film or play with ease unless it is subtitled or they have STAGETEXT available, and they have searched out less demanding activities, such as exploring museums and art galleries.

If you are unable to access the information at these latter venues, remind those responsible about the Disability Discrimination Act 1995 (DDA) which states, 'It is unlawful for a service provider to discriminate by offering a lower standard of service or providing a service in a worse manner to disabled people.' For residents and visitors to London there is an organisation called MAGIC (Museums and Galleries in the Capital – see Appendix 1), which provides information about programmes that have communication support at London's museums and galleries.

Suggestions for managing your inability to understand speech in difficult listening conditions have already been described in Chapter 16. In this chapter we are focusing on two of the most common problems that are constantly brought to our attention – attending get-togethers and eating socially in restaurants. To illustrate some possible solutions we have drawn on the experiences of people we have met, and for whom a loss of hearing, although extremely frustrating, has inadvertently provided an opportunity to try another way to continue with the activities they enjoy. We have also listed the hobbies and interests that have given pleasure to the people we have met and which are less reliant on the spoken word for a satisfying experience.

The chair of a wine club was unable to participate easily in the group discussions at meetings, and he therefore chose to step down and concentrate on making his own wine. He became so successful that he had a question and answer page in the club newsletter. He researched the answers enthusiastically, and this was an activity he was able to carry out in his own home. When he did attend meetings he felt more in control, because he felt he could anticipate questions more readily as a result of his new learning.

A married couple enjoyed exploring historic towns. The wife became profoundly deafened as a result of meningitis, and it was difficult to walk and lipread because of the hazards of uneven pavements, etc. Instead the couple decided to walk in the countryside, and eventually walked the whole South Coast Path of England, taking advantage of the wide cliff paths to walk side by side, which was better for lipreading.

Jack started to lose his hearing in his early thirties and it took him 20 years to accept that he was unable to enjoy his hobby of attending classical music concerts. The tunes he remembered were nothing like the sound he could hear. He became upset and took long solitary walks to ease his frustration. Without realising why, he began to look forward to these, savouring the rhythm and the movement of his legs and the wind and sun in his face. Around the same time he started taking more photographs to capture the beauty of the countryside. He also developed a growing interest in home decorating, relishing the opportunity to demonstrate his visual skills. For relaxation he turned to jigsaws and crosswords. They were all a pleasure for him and he felt satisfied about his achievements. Unknowingly, he had gravitated towards relaxing pursuits, which involved less communication. His new hobbies were fairly inexpensive; he had not wanted to spend his capital on a new camera because his old one was adequate for his needs. He discovered that, instead of becoming engaged in conversations he could not understand, he could be usefully occupied taking photographs of the social events he had once avoided. He could provide a pictorial record of any occasion or photographs for greetings cards. He felt satisfied and involved with his family and friends and, most importantly of all, had lowered his expectations.

Pleasures and hobbies that do not totally rely on hearing

As you can see, the people featured in these three case histories changed their pleasure pursuits to accommodate the limitations imposed by their hearing loss. We have therefore compiled a list of pleasures and hobbies that do not totally rely on hearing for information, education and entertainment, which you may like to consider.

◆ Beekeeping
◆ Carpentry
◆ Crosswords
◆ Cycling
◆ DIY
◆ Filming
◆ Jigsaws
◆ Lectures in places of interest that arrange communication support –lipspeaker, loop and infrared system
◆ Painting
◆ Photography
◆ Reading
◆ Researching family trees
◆ Stamp collecting
◆ Theatre with STAGETEXT
◆ Travel
◆ Visiting museums and art galleries that have text versions of audio-recorded information, sound enhancement systems (induction loops and infrared systems)
◆ Walking
◆ Watching TV, DVDs and videos with closed captions.

Attending a party

Some situations will always be difficult if you are deaf or hard of hearing, especially when there are a lot of people in the vicinity. However, some planning and careful weighing up of the situation once you arrive may help. When deciding on your best strategies you should consider: lighting, source of noise, acoustics of the room, and how you can get some enjoyment out of the situation.

Lighting

In order to make the most of visual clues to speech, including lipreading, you need to have the light on the face of the speaker. Look for the sources of light. Avoid dim areas of a room. Turn your own back to the light.

Source of noise

Notice where the music comes from and avoid it. Notice where sounds of china, cutlery, etc. come from and move away if you can. In the middle of the room, the sound of conversation will be all around you, so try to get a wall behind you, or even better soft furnishings such as curtains. There is always disturbance and distraction near a door, as people come and go – move away if you can. In noisy situations everybody will be speaking more loudly, so you may find it easier to turn down the volume on your hearing aid, or even to take it out altogether and rely on your natural hearing helped by lipreading.

Acoustics of the room

Hearing aids often make all sounds louder, including echoes. Sound waves rebound off hard surfaces causing confused and distorted sound. If possible, avoid rooms such as kitchens or places without carpets, curtains or upholstered furniture, which all help to absorb reflected sounds (see Chapter 11).

How you can get some enjoyment out of the situation

Think about these strategies and try some out.

- Arrive in plenty of time so you can find the best place in the room for you.
- Try to speak 'one to one' with people.
- Avoid large groups where there is a lot of cross-talking.
- Stay with people who intimate that they want to talk to you and do not mind repeating things.
- Explain why you need to watch the speaker's face.
- Enlist the help of a friend, especially when you need to know the subject of a conversation you have just joined.
- Do not try to eat and converse at the same time.
- Take a quiet break, rest, and enjoy your food.
- When you get tired or it gets too noisy, acknowledge this and go home.

Giving a party

This is sometimes easier, because you are likely to be more in control and can arrange all the changes that will help with communication.

- Send guests all details of the event in writing.
- Have a theme for the party – it will possibly be a good conversation piece offering more familiar clues to ease conversation.

- Arrange a game reliant on written information for the clues.
- Control numbers and situation.
- Lay out the buffet at the end of the hall or kitchen, not in the party room.
- Place food and drink on a thick tablecloth with felt or newspaper underneath to deaden the clatter of dishes.
- Have the party in a room with thick carpets, soft chairs and sofas – heavy curtains absorb sound and help deaden background noise.
- Keep lighting up and ban music.
- Be determined to be a part of your party and adopt a positive attitude. Wear something striking to attract attention.
- Give yourself permission to leave your party and have an eye break for five minutes.

Eating in a restaurant

If you are having a meal with someone you can lipread, and perhaps hear because you know them well, then you will probably be managing to understand them and will really enjoy the meal. However, if you are having a meal with someone you have not met before the following suggestions will be useful.

- Choose a restaurant with plenty of light and soft furnishings.
- If possible contact the restaurant and ask for a table in a well-lit corner away from the kitchen.
- Arrange to eat at the earliest time when there are fewer people being served.
- Arrive early to choose the place where you prefer to sit.
- Avoid a restaurant with live entertainment.
- Ask to have the background music turned down.
- Avoid having a meal with more than eight people.
- If you are comfortable about doing so, advise everyone at the table that you have a hearing loss.
- Choose a meal from the main menu or ask for a written copy of the 'specials' list.
- Use a personal listening system.
- Sit with your back to the wall to minimise background noise.
- Sit where you can see everyone.
- Try not to sit facing a bright light.
- Lipreading and eating at the same time is difficult.
- Lipreading somebody who is eating is difficult.

The figure opposite shows various seating plans in a restaurant.

Taking a break with family, friends and colleagues

In your own surroundings

- Sit with your back to the light and where you can see the other people.
- Move the furniture around if necessary. (It is a good idea to have chairs on castors for this purpose.)
- Suggest you move to a room in your home where there is a carpet or plenty of mats.
- Use cups and saucers and place a tissue or a small doily between the cup and saucer.
- Turn on the lights if it is dark or shadowy.

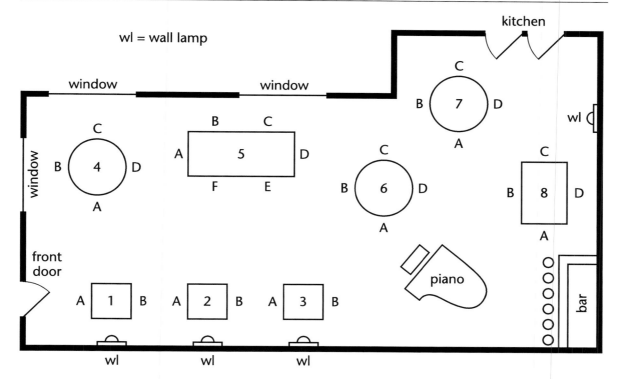

Look at this diagram and answer the following questions:
1. Which table would you prefer? Why?
2. Which table is your second choice? Why?
3. What is wrong with the following tables? 1, 3, 5, 7, 8.
4. Suppose you are seated at table 2 for lunch. What would make it easier for conversation?

- Avoid sitting beside someone on a settee – it may be difficult to lipread them from the side.
- If using a coffee table, cover it with a thick cloth.
- Turn off the TV or radio.
- If you become tired because you are lipreading take a break.

Out and about

- Arrive early and choose a quiet well-lit spot.
- If you arrive with your companions, explain your difficulties.
- Sit next to someone you know well and ask them to keep you informed about the
  conversation if you start to get lost.
- Take a pad and pen at all times.

Answers to questions

1. 4C. The table is round, near two windows and away from other tables.
2. 5B or 5C. The seats are away from other tables. The window is behind them.
3. 1 is near the front door; 3 is near the piano; 6 is near the piano and other tables; 7 is near the kitchen door; 8 is near the piano, bar and kitchen door.
4. Ask to have the seats changed round so the light is behind A or B.

Chapter 20

Travel

Holidays and hearing loss

Holidays are by definition a period of relaxation, recreation and cheerfulness. A time for family, friends and acquaintances to be together and share new experiences and reflect on the day's events. A change in the capabilities of your senses, such as a loss of hearing, may cause some problems when you are adjusting to the unexpected difficulties encountered in the novel and unfamiliar situations that characterise holidays. Communication is a two-way process, and the travelling companion of a person with a hearing loss may become resentful when this breaks down. This can be avoided if all concerned are more honest about their needs as early as possible, instead of becoming increasingly frustrated through a lack of understanding and preparation.

Even travelling for short distances may give rise to anxieties, such as not knowing how to contact somebody when you are running late because of transport delays. Fortunately technology has progressed to the point that nearly nine out of ten people now use a mobile phone, and deaf and hard of hearing people can use them to send a text message.

In a recent case known to us, a college lecturer who had become profoundly deaf over a period of two years was becoming increasingly anxious about travelling for business or pleasure, because he dreaded being late for a presentation or missing a plane. Prior to his loss of hearing he had relied on announcements, and overhearing other people, for information about what was happening. He told us that he could not use a mobile phone because of his deafness. It was only when we discussed his concerns at length that he realised he would be able to use a mobile phone for text messaging in order to contact his colleagues and friends – all of whom had been urging him to purchase one for some time.

Another example of feeling isolated, by not being able to gain information by overhearing, was when an 80-year-old London man who relied on two powerful hearing aids, to hear any sound, became frustrated when he was unable to find out if London's bid to host the 2012 Olympics had been successful. He did not know his home city had been chosen until eight o'clock the next morning when he read the newspaper. He was touring North Wales on the train and had not seen any headlines because of the remoteness of his journey. The television in the hotel bedroom did not have Teletext so he did not bother to watch it. However, he relied, as always, for information from his daily paper.

Hearing aid users are particularly vulnerable while travelling on holiday. Even high quality hearing aids do not function equally well in background noise. Demands on communication strategies are enormous. Confidence in the hearing aid diminishes as the unexpected occurs. A few examples of this are:

◆ The hearing aid is not functioning.
◆ An unexpected change in travel arrangements is not understood.
◆ A fellow traveller starts to talk about something interesting they have seen just as an aircraft flies overhead.

♦ A child shrieks with happiness causing acute discomfort for some hearing aid users.

These are all pitfalls that are not always easily rectified but which could be better understood and coped with if information was available to help alleviate some of these experiences. We have collected the following strategies which you may find useful.

Preparing for a holiday

♦ If you have access to the internet, make your booking online. You will receive a written itinerary and there will be fewer misunderstandings.

♦ Check your hearing aid.

♦ Pack a supply of spare batteries, plastic tubing, a puffer or pipe cleaner and, if possible, a spare hearing aid (see the section on How to look after your hearing aid in Chapter 10).

♦ Pack enough medication for the whole time you are away, since chemists may not always stock prescription items. If you get a cold, use nasal decongestants recommended by a medical practitioner.

♦ Prepare two clearly written cards. On one indicate clearly how people can help you understand them in the language of the country being visited. On the second print details of who to contact in case of an accident and inability to communicate with hospital staff, etc.

♦ Label all luggage clearly.

♦ Write your postcode or zip code only on your label.

♦ Use a piece of material or a strap with a bright colour (yellow on black is one of the most visual combinations) to make your luggage easy to identify.

♦ Photocopy all documents (including tickets).

♦ Ensure the voltage of equipment such as a flashing light or a vibrating alarm clock is compatible with the country being visited and take a plug adapter, or use battery-operated equipment.

♦ If you use your laptop for email pack a high speed internet modem cable for use in a hotel room that has a data point.

♦ Include a door beacon in your luggage which is a battery-operated flashing device to alert you to a knock at the door. It is clipped over the top of the door and has a built in sensor which acts in response to the vibration.

♦ Take extra travel adapters for charging computers, mobile phones, etc. For most European countries Euro adapters are required.

♦ Remember to put all sharp instruments such as scissors and knives in your main luggage, not your hand luggage. Security is very strict on all airlines and you may become involved in a conversation that you were not prepared for.

♦ **Discuss all the travel arrangements with a travelling companion before departure**. For example, it is difficult to discuss this type of information while driving a car because of the background noise, and it can be dangerous to attempt to lipread because you will take your eyes off the road. Make sure the exact name of your destination, accommodation and travel times are written down, leaving space for further information to be added. If a difficult situation occurs you have this available to show somebody where you are going. Ask them to write down directions if necessary.

♦ Self-catering holidays offer privacy and the choice of eating in quieter conditions if you prefer. Eating in a hotel restaurant can be very difficult because of the poor acoustics caused by the reflection of sound waves created by uncarpeted floors, Formica-topped tables and plate glass windows. Also the background noise created by other holidaymakers can severely interfere with your understanding of speech, especially as this is a time when the day's events are likely to be discussed.

♦ If possible ask for a room at the back of the hotel, because traffic noise heard in the bedroom can be very stressful. That is because it is the perfect place to share and enjoy the experiences of the day with a travelling companion. The soft furnishings in the bedroom absorb sound and create an ideal situation for listening.

- When booking a holiday, ask for a television with subtitle facilities and a video recorder (for watching the videos you have recorded with subtitles at home and have not got round to watching) to be placed in the room if possible.
- Consider carefully the effect of including children in a holiday. Their excited chatter may make communication at meal times difficult, and it could become very frustrating not to understand the conversation around the table, while it would be unfair to ask the children to refrain from talking. This could lead to a highly stressful situation, which might not be rectified until communication conditions improve, and by then the feelings of resentment generated may be acute. It takes a stable relationship to cope with such unanticipated occurrences.
- Research the intended destination prior to departure so that you are aware of cultural and climatic differences that may have an impact on the holiday.
- When you are eating in restaurants remember that in hotter countries, especially in Europe, they can often be very noisy with stone floors, walls and ceilings. Also children are tolerated and welcomed to much later hours, and in some countries people start eating very much later in the evening. Therefore restaurants may be quiet to begin with, but much noisier later on. Try to arrive early if possible.

General

- Wait close to staff at the point of departure to give yourself the best chance to notice visual and aural clues relating to any vital changes in travel arrangements.
- It may not be easy to engage in a conversation while out and about. To overcome this significant difficulty try to identify somewhere quiet to sit and talk as frequently as time allows.
- When travelling with an organised party, consider wearing a hard of hearing badge.

On the trip

Coach

- Advise the driver or courier about your communication requirements because of your hearing loss. Make sure you are kept informed by co-opting other passengers. During coach stops ask about the time to return to the coach and where the check-out is and write it down.
- Look for visual indicators and study these.
- Record the details of your coach, e.g. company, colour, make and registration. In large continental coach parks and autobahn stops, it is easy to get confused and you will not have time to become familiar with the layout of coach booking halls and bays, etc.

Train

- Carry a timetable for the journey with any necessary changes marked by the travel centre – do not rely on booking clerks or station staff. Check the details when the ticket is inspected. If the journey is complicated, get all the information in writing. Place names are sometimes difficult to lipread and station tannoys are frequently impossible to understand, even for a person with normal hearing.
- Avoid a last minute panic by making a note of the carriage and seat number on the palm of your hand for instant recognition.

- Arrive early at the station to be one of the first on the train to avoid not being able to find a reserved seat or room for luggage.
- If there are engineering works on the line ask to have all the information about changes written down.

Ship

- Ticket requirements are much the same as on trains but with the added problem of boarding cards.
- Locate the ship's purser's office immediately upon boarding. If in any difficulty, e.g. which deck to disembark from, rely on the purser.
- Some ships have single sex cabins with four or six berths, which will probably involve sharing. A hearing impairment may mean that a person could be particularly vulnerable to theft when asleep. If this is likely to be a problem, ask the purser to take care of any valuables, or get VIP treatment in special cabins.
- If you disembark to visit a place, write down the time you have to return.

Plane

- Prebook your seat away from the engines – otherwise there is a degraded signal-to-noise ratio as well vibration from the engines, particularly of older aircraft. Sit well back in the plane alongside the gangway if possible.
- Arrive early at the airport to allow yourself plenty of time for booking in. Inform airline check-in staff about your hearing loss, and remember that you may not hear announcements made during the journey.
- Advise the air crew about your hearing loss and the need to receive every announced message personally. Most will have been trained in helping hearing impaired passengers and will appreciate the practice.
- Watch other passengers for clues about seat belts, smoking, life jackets, etc.
- Remove or switch off your hearing aid during take off and landing. Advise travelling companions about this. Compression pains in the ear are quite normal and affect normal hearing passengers also. The sound of your tinnitus may change, but again this is quite normal and it should disappear when the plane lands.

Arrival

- Lipreading and listening to amplified sound may be tiring. It is therefore a good idea after finding your accommodation to either remove or switch off your hearing aid and have a rest before tackling any new communication situations.
- Try not to be oversensitive about your loss of hearing, and find a way that feels comfortable to inform others about your communication needs and how they can help.
- If you are travelling with a hearing companion, explain at the outset the limitations created by a hearing loss in order to minimise any misunderstandings.
- Purchase a street map of the resort, particularly if it is in a country where an unfamiliar language is spoken. Carry this all the time to avoid having to ask for directions on a busy road.
- At the hotel, ensure that the receptionist notes any special requirements related to your hearing loss, including your inability to hear fire alarms.
- If you are in the UK, remind them about the Disability Discrimination Act if necessary. This states that hotels must make 'reasonable adjustments' to any barriers that may prevent a disabled person using or accessing their services. One adjustment recommended is that the hotel should provide portable vibrating alarms for guests who will not be able to hear an audible fire alarm.
- You may be allocated a room on the ground floor – this may not be the most

suitable because of the risk of not hearing an intruder. Ask at reception for a room on a higher floor explaining the reason why. If this is not possible, ask a travelling companion to hold a spare room key. On the other hand a ground floor room may make it easier for staff to help you in an emergency.

◆ When sharing a room, discuss the allocation of storage space on arrival – preferably by sitting down and deciding this before there are misunderstandings caused by the difficulty of lipreading when moving around the room. Switch on all the lights to help with lipreading, especially if the room is long and narrow with the main window at the end.

◆ Many hotels have email facilities in the reception area and data points in the rooms. For a small charge these are available for communicating with friends and family at home and accessing the internet.

◆ Some hotels may have textphones which can be placed in the room on request.

Out and about

Sightseeing

◆ Obtain as much information about the place to be visited as early as possible.
◆ Maximise use of listening aids – ask the leader of a tour to wear the transmitter of your radio aid.
◆ Stand at the front of the group.
◆ Be aware that overhead power lines and some roadside generators may interfere with your hearing aid. This is not an inherent fault with the aid and the interference will lessen as soon as they are passed.

On the beach

◆ Do not get sand or water in the hearing aid – both can stop it functioning.
◆ Keep your sunglasses handy for lipreading.
◆ Remember to remove your hearing aids when swimming. Advise others that speech and warning sounds may not be heard, but also be extra careful about boats or jet skis, etc. that may be around.

Rambling

◆ Walking in a town or along a main road can be hazardous. It may be difficult to understand speech through your hearing aid because of the background noise.
◆ Walking two abreast to facilitate lipreading can be dangerous on a narrow pavement, especially if your loss of hearing is accompanied by vertigo.
◆ Walking in a forest or open countryside is more conducive to communication, as speech can be heard more clearly because of the undercarpet of natural vegetation.
◆ If you sweat easily whilst walking energetically, the tubing of your hearing aid may become blocked with condensation. Remove your hearing aid, and tell the rest of the party that you have done this so that they know you will not be able to understand them so well.

The weather

◆ Cold weather, either at high altitudes or in normal winter conditions, may suddenly affect your hearing aid. Remove the battery and rub briskly with a handkerchief.
◆ Wet weather can make the background noise created by car wheels sound much louder than normal, because of the swish of rubber tyres on a wet surface. This is more noticeable in places where the roads are cobbled or enclosed within high walls.

◆ The noise of the wind has a tendency to drown out other sounds.

◆ Hot or cold weather may cause condensation in the tube connecting the ear mould to your hearing aid and may stop it functioning. Clean this out with a pipe cleaner or simply disconnect the tubing from the hard elbow and blow through it.

A challenging holiday situation

The long anticipated holiday had arrived. The journey by taxi to the station, and then by train to the airport, and finally the minibus to the ship, had all gone smoothly. Bill and Sheila were looking forward to having all their meals provided for them. Breakfast and lunch were to be a buffet, and dinner in the evening was a set meal. On arrival at breakfast they were given a table number, which had to be used for the evening meal; at all other times they could sit where they wanted.

In the evening they found their table and sat down with another couple who were already in animated conversation and broke off when Bill and Sheila introduced themselves. It quickly became obvious that Bill was in trouble. He was wearing two digital hearing aids, and when he turned to lipread the man next to him, he was completely unable to do so because the late evening sun was shining directly into his eyes. He had forgotten to bring his communicator and the background noise from other passengers was loud through his aids. To make matters worse he was unable to lipread the woman passenger opposite because she had long hair and thin lips. She was already starting to look distinctly uncomfortable about being interrupted. A valiant attempt at conversation on all sides failed miserably. Bill was completely lost, and although his wife did her best to keep him informed about the conversation, she too was becoming tired because it was difficult to repeat important statements without being patronising or losing the meaning. It was also extremely demanding to speak clearly and eat at the same time. The couple were looking distinctly uncomfortable too, and at one point the woman snapped, 'We were hoping to have a table to ourselves.' After eating dessert in uncomfortable silence, Bill and Sheila hastily left the table feeling exhausted, frustrated and determined to ask for another table on their own for future meals. They were also very aware that the couple were on holiday and did not appear inclined to make an effort to include Bill, and indeed did not know how to do so! It had been a difficult experience for all involved.

This situation described here could have been at a wedding, or a meal in a busy restaurant. What do you think you could do to anticipate this happening? Tick the answers that you think could have been most helpful for you.

◆ Ask for a table for two on arrival. ❑

◆ Remember to take a personal listening system (see Chapter 21). ❑

◆ Ask to change seats and sit with the light behind you. ❑

◆ Ask for a table in the corner of the restaurant. ❑

◆ Tell the people at the table immediately that you have a hearing problem. ❑

◆ Take a note pad and pen and ask the other people at the table to let you know what they are talking about. ❑

◆ Move the chairs in order to be able to see everyone. ❑

◆ Check the acoustics of the venue first. ❑

◆ Wear a badge indicating you have a hearing loss. ❑

Chapter 21

Aids to daily living equipment

Aids to daily living equipment, Assistive Listening Devices (ALDS), Environmental Aids or Equipment for deaf and hard of hearing people are all alternative descriptions for the extra pieces of equipment enabling a person with a hearing loss to access sounds that hearing people take for granted. If you:

◆ have difficulty understanding speech on the radio, television and telephone;
◆ do not always hear the telephone or doorbell ring;
◆ worry all the time that you will not hear your baby cry;
◆ often wake up late in the morning because you have not heard the alarm,

the information in this chapter will be of use to you:

As mentioned in Chapter 9 we use our hearing to inform and alert us to speech and environmental sounds. These sounds can be replaced by using a suitable alternative piece of equipment that will help you get on with your daily tasks.

There is a wide range of products available and we have listed these under four general headings and added four examples of how they can be used to enable you to preserve your independence, dignity and freedom, a perspective we have also written about in Chapter 12.

How to obtain the equipment

The first thing to do is to contact your local social services department and ask them to assess your needs. The officer will then suggest which equipment will be the most helpful for you. You may be provided with this equipment free of charge within the terms of the Social Services contract, or you may be advised that you need to pay for it. This is because the contract is based on need and your personal circumstances will be taken into account within the assessment. For example, if you are a mother with two or three young children, one of whom may be a new baby, it is likely you will be offered a paging system of some kind. If you live alone, and cannot hear the doorbell, you may be in the habit of leaving your door open; this is deemed to be a critical situation, and you will be offered a flashing light or louder doorbell.

If you decide to buy the equipment, you will find that you will be exempt from paying VAT if you are deaf or hard of hearing. Advise the supplier of this when you order the equipment and they should be able to send you a VAT exemption form to fill in. Some manufacturers and suppliers also allow you a trial period.

You may get a list of equipment and their manufacturers and suppliers from the following sources:

◆ local audiology department
◆ local Hearing Therapist
◆ local private hearing aid dispenser
◆ local lipreading teacher
◆ local hard of hearing group

◆ local librarian
◆ local social services.

Alternatively enter 'deaf and hard of hearing equipment' into your internet search facility and access the information you require, or read the information in the glossary.
Equipment is available in four different categories: alerting; listening; tele-communication; video.

Alerting

To warn you that the telephone is ringing or someone is at the door, visual, tactile (something you feel) and amplified signals are available. The equipment below is all obtainable with either an extra loud sound, different tone, flashing light or an integral or external vibrating element.

Different types of alarms and alerters

◆ Alarms – baby, fire, personal call, smoke alarm or detector, wake up alarms
◆ Alerters – door bell, telephone bell.

These are available as single pieces of equipment or as multi-alerting (paging systems) whereby a transmitter picks up the warning sound and sends a radio signal to the receiver, which vibrates and alerts you to which one is being activated. Red lights or numbers on the receiver indicate the sound that has activated the system.

◆ Door knocking alerter or Door Beacon
◆ Analogue and digital vibrating wrist watches, which can be set to alert you to several events during the day.

Listening

Personal listening systems are useful when you wish to have the volume of sound on the television or that of the person you are listening to made louder. They are available as portable small individual hand sets that allow you to adjust the level of sound to suit your needs and without affecting anyone nearby. Head phones, stetoclips, ear buds or a loop are used to receive the sound. They are available as:

◆ Light weight individual *battery powered units* connected to the source of sound.
◆ *Wireless infrared TV listeners*, which operate within the same room as the sound source by using infrared signals – there are no trailing wires and there are models for non-hearing aid wearers and hearing aids wearers.
◆ *Loop amplifying systems* for use with your hearing aid and which enable you to benefit from pure undistorted sound without distracting background noises; they are a bit like a radio signal that the hearing aid can pick up and are particularly helpful for receiving speech on the television. There are loop systems for use on an individual chair or round the edge of a living room, in a car or as a meeting aid in a discreet folder. Other uses for the loop are in large rooms during meetings, performances, etc. They are also used in banks, post offices and building societies, where a cross-counter loop is provided to enable you to have private and confiden-tial interaction. A loop system may also be used in a theatre, place of worship, community hall or conference room.
◆ *Radio aids and FM (frequency modulation) systems* to help remove the background noise between a hard of hearing person and the speaker. They require a special 'shoe' to be fitted to the hearing aid to receive the signal – a small module that

clips onto the bottom of the aid. They are particularly useful for individual conversations and in educational settings. Radio aids (but not FM) systems are used by setting the hearing aid to the 'T' position.

Telecommunication

You may be experiencing difficulties understanding speech on the telephone. If you are a non-hearing aid wearer, this problem is frequently helped by using a telephone with an adjustable volume control for incoming speech. For a hearing aid wearer an inductive coupler in the handset will enable you to amplify the incoming sound using the 'T' facility on your hearing aid. This will activate the internal microphone of your hearing aid and enable you to hear the speaker better by eliminating background noise such as traffic noise and the sound of the television.

A variety of telephones with these features are available including cordless models. Features such as big buttons, portable amplifiers and a louder ring tone are also available.

If you are unable to understand speech on the telephone then you may find a text phone more helpful. You will be able to send and receive a message, which will be displayed on a small display screen.

Mobile phones can be used with a loop wire plugged into the bottom, to enable you to understand speech better, again using the 'T' facility on your hearing aid. Some also have an integral amplifier in the neck loop.

Video phones enable you to have a video conversation as long as the other person has similar features on their phone.

Video and DVD

◆ *Video recorders* record the subtitled programmes.
◆ *Video caption readers* enable you to watch prerecorded videos which have had sub-titles added. The following symbol denotes the video has subtitles and caption display.

◆ *DVD players* fixed and portable enable you to enjoy a film with subtitles that are available on most DVDs, with the exception of free offers that come with many newspapers.

Jill has enrolled on a full-time course at her local college to study to become a beautician. She has been wearing two hearing aids since she was 10-years-old when she contracted meningitis. As part of the enrolment process she was given the opportunity to see the Learning Support Co-ordinator who recommended she was provided with a radio aid to enable her to understand the lectures and practical sessions without the interference of the background noise of traffic outside the college.

Ann is in her late twenties. She has been almost profoundly deaf for many years; her hearing aids gave her a sense of being connected to the world but she was not always able to distinguish between different speech and alerting sounds. She was interviewed for a more senior role in her place of work and, although she knew she possessed the skills and knowledge to perform the task, was aware that her hearing had deteriorated recently, and took the opportunity to ask for some improvements to be made, to enable her to understand speech to the best of her ability both with colleagues and customers. The promotion involved her being given an office of her own and some additional training. Because of the government's Access to Work scheme she was able to receive new hearing aids that matched her hearing loss better: a text phone to contact customers via Type Talk; a strobe fire alarm; a flashing door beacon to enable her to know that someone was at her office door and a radio aid to help her understand speech better in meetings.

John became almost profoundly deaf in a short space of time. He had contracted a virus and had been told that there was no medicine or surgery that could restore his hearing. His vision was also affected, and he had to have a stronger prescription for his glasses. He was issued with two hearing aids. His wife had been ill for many years and was confined to a wheelchair, she was dependent on John for her care. Before he became hard of hearing John was able to hear his wife call for him and understand what she was saying when he was in another room. As a result of losing his hearing he had to adjust to the unfamiliar sound through his hearing aid and find alternative ways of knowing when his wife needed him. He contacted his local social services and he was provided with a telephone with an amplifier and an inductive coupler in the handset, which enabled him to amplify the sound through his hearing aid using the 'T' facility. The telephone also had large buttons to help him see the numbers he wanted more easily. He was also given a multi-alerting paging system enabling him to carry on with his daily routine without missing the sound of the door and telephone bell and when his wife required his assistance. He knew which system had been activated by the number that was illuminated on the top of the pager.

Edward's wife died after 46 years of marriage. He lives in a semi-detached house. He has a severe hearing loss as a result of working on the heavy guns in the Navy during his national service. He uses a body-worn hearing aid. Before his wife died she would always hear the door and telephone bell and respond to the calls. She also told him when the sound on the TV was too loud. After a while the neighbours complained that his TV was too loud and his daughter became worried because he had often not answered the door or the telephone when she tried to contact him. She suggested he contacted social services for an assessment of his needs. He was supplied with a loop system for the TV and was able to listen to the TV through his hearing aids and adjust the sound on the loop amplifying unit to suit his needs. A phone with an amplifier and inductive coupler were also provided, as was a portable flashing light door bell and a louder extension bell for his telephone. He was also given a smoke alarm with a strobe light in all his main rooms with the addition of a vibrating disc to place beneath his pillow to alert him at night when he was not able to hear anything. His family bought him a DVD player which he found difficult to manage at first, but soon became used to it and was able to watch many of his favourite classical comedy programmes with subtitles. He was able to retain his independence and dignity and his daughter was less worried about his inability to hear.

Chapter 22

Solutions for unanticipated situations

Here are some common problems that can occur, with some possible solutions.

Battery goes dead in the middle of something important
- Change battery before leaving home.
- Always carry a spare pack of batteries with you.
- Carry a battery tester.

Unable to understand a stranger who is serving you in shop/bank/railway station, especially behind glass
- Get them to write the information down.
- Tell them you are deaf.
- Ask them to speak more slowly.

Being approached in a crowded room with a lot of background noise by a person who wants to talk and you cannot hear
- Take the person into a quiet corner where it will be easier to converse.

Unable to understand a waiter
- Ask your companion to repeat what was said.
- If you are on your own, point to the item in the menu, and show it to the waiter as you ask about it.
- Avoid asking about the dish of the day in case the waiter speaks too fast and you are not able to take it all in.

Unexpected questions in a shop
'Do you want the hangers/cashback/help with your luggage/two for the price of one?'
- Go to the check-out which has an 'inductive loop' system and switch your hearing aid to the 'T' position if it has one.
- Ask for what you want before they speak to you.
- Tell them you are deaf and cannot hear what they are saying, and ask them to repeat what they said.
- Be patient and do not panic – most shop assistants want to help if you let them.
- Watch the body language of the person serving you.
- Always check for signs around the shop before you make your purchase.

Meeting someone in the street and not knowing what they have said
- Tell them there and then that you don't understand because of background noise or whatever has caused the problem.
- Don't leave them in the air wondering why you were behaving oddly.
- Arrange to get in touch by email or letter if appropriate. A suggested approach is: 'It was really nice to meet you. I didn't catch all of what you said. Please fill me in on your news.'

Unable to understand someone who is very distressed

◆ If they are in need of help there and then, try not to worry about your inability to hear. Try to help immediately, and possibly ask for assistance from a passing stranger.

◆ Use a sympathetic expression and body language.

◆ Contact a mutual friend afterwards and ask what is going on.

Not understanding speech on telephone

◆ Use 'T' switch on hearing aid.

◆ Purchase or rent an amplified telephone.

◆ Learn to use a textphone or email.

◆ Ask people to speak slowly.

◆ After the caller has announced themselves, make sure your first words are 'I am rather hard of hearing, so when you speak please be kind enough to speak up.'

Neighbours complain television is too loud

◆ Use subtitles, or television amplifiers, or earphones.

◆ Move television away from adjoining wall.

◆ Purchase a loop system.

Doorbell not always heard

◆ Purchase a louder/different tone/visual/vibrating doorbell.

Background music in restaurant

◆ Ask them to turn it down and explain why.

◆ Make sure you sit as far away from the loudspeakers as possible.

Worried about coping at a meal with other people

◆ Ask for a table with a tablecloth to deaden sound.

◆ Sit at the table where you can see everyone.

◆ Ask for a table away from the kitchen.

◆ Ask for a corner table.

◆ Sit with your back to the wall or with no one behind you.

◆ Try to use a restaurant with curtains and carpets.

◆ Be straightforward – tell everyone you have a hearing loss.

Hearing aid whistles

◆ Is it in properly?

◆ Have you got wax in your ear?

◆ Is it loose?

◆ Have you got the sound turned up too loud?

◆ Is the tubing twisted?

◆ Does the ear mould need washing?

Hearing traffic when crossing road

◆ Always use a crossing and look carefully both ways.

◆ Wear your hearing aid all the time.

Hearing your name being called in a GP's waiting room

◆ Ask receptionist to come and get you. Work out between you what is the easiest way for this to happen.

◆ Sit near the door of the doctor.

◆ If you are given a number, hold this in front of you.

◆ If your GP's surgery or local hospital does not have one, urge them to get a visual screen that lets you know when it is your turn.

© HEARING CONCERN　www.hearingconcern.org.uk

Unable to hear at the hairdressers
- Advise your hairdresser you have a difficulty with your hearing, and that you might not understand what they are asking you.
- Let them know that once you take your aids out you will be completely deaf.
- Advise them to ask you things only while you are looking at them.
- Try to lipread by looking in the mirror.

Unable to hear announcements in public areas
- Ask a friendly looking person to tell you what is going on.
- Keep a paper and pencil with you for accurate information.
- Sit near the notice, indicator board or television screen.
- Seek out a member of staff and ask what is happening.

Unable to understand the service in a place of worship
- Sit in the front.
- Ask for a copy of the sermon.
- Ensure any loop system is installed and switched on.

Unable to wake up in the morning
- Purchase a flashing light, vibrating or louder ringing alarm clock.
- Sleep with the curtains open so you wake up at dawn.
- Last thing at night repeat frequently 'I must wake at…in the morning'.

Hearing aid not helpful for understanding speech
- Return to your audiology department or the firm where you received your hearing aid and have it checked.
- Watch the speaker's face and body language when they are talking to you.
- Ensure you have a T switch on your hearing aid and the system is activated.

TV programmes background music too loud
- Write to the broadcasters.

Unable to hear when you have dropped something
- Be on the alert all the time.
- Look around before you leave.
- Do not overfill your pockets.
- Store articles in their correct container.
- Affix spectacles, keys, mobile phones, etc. to your person.

Unable to hear emergency vehicles until they are very near
- Place extra car mirrors strategically and use them often.
- Keep sound distractions to the minimum.
- Observe other road users.

Difficulty understanding conversation in the car
- Place an extra large adjustable mirror in the middle of the front windscreen.
- Use a portable seat loop or Converser.
- Tell people not to speak to you while you are driving.
- Stopping people shouting when you say you cannot hear.
- Ask them to speak more slowly and in a slightly louder voice.
- Tell them you have a hearing loss and rely on lipreading: ask them to speak clearly.

Difficulty understanding speech in the theatre and cinema
- Join the STAGETEXT mailing list to find out which theatre is showing a captioned performance near you.

◆ Go to subtitles@yourlocalcinema.com and look at the list of subtitled films that are on in your area.

◆ If you use a hearing aid with a T position on the switch, check whether the cinema or theatre has a loop system. Alternatively they may have an infrared listening device, which can be used with or without your hearing aid.

◆ Before you attend, obtain a synopsis or read the book of the film or play.

© Hearing Concern   www.hearingconcern.org.uk

Chapter 23

Advice for hearing people

All of us are potentially disabled people. Health and strength, which we take for granted, can be taken away from us at any time by illness or accident. If we are fortunate enough to live into old age we shall probably all have some health problem to cope with – diabetes, heart trouble, cataracts, arthritis. So we should not think of disability and ability as a 'them and us' situation. We are all of us on a path from ability to disability. Once we realise this, it affects our attitudes to people with disabilities.

Hearing loss is the second largest disability – mobility is the largest. There are nine million deaf and hard of hearing people in the United Kingdom; 55% of people over 60 and 93.2% of people over 80 are deaf or hard of hearing.[1] In practical terms this means that if you meet seven people in the course of your day, at least one of them will be hard of hearing or deaf. If you are sitting reading this in a busy place, look round and make a quick estimate of the number of people near you. How many of these people could be deaf? Think of the implications of this for you and for them!

If deafness is so common, why are we not more aware of it? Deafness, like many other health problems, is invisible. For example, you cannot tell if someone has diabetes just by looking at them. This explains why you sometimes see car stickers that read – 'Watch out for that child – he may be deaf!' You cannot tell if a child is deaf by looking at him or her. A deaf child may run out into the road because they did not hear the car coming. It is no use the motorist just sounding his horn as a warning – a deaf child will not hear and get out of the way. It is sensible to sound the horn and take evasive action. In the same way, an elderly lady walking along the pavement may not move when she hears a cyclist coming along behind her. It is no use the cyclist sounding his bell or shouting. If she is hard of hearing or deaf she will not move because she has not heard the warning.

Deafness is often mistaken for something else – bad manners, inattention, confusion or lack of intelligence. A hard of hearing person may be accused of being 'rude', 'stuck-up' or 'uncaring' – when in fact they are very polite, modest and thoughtful. They just did not hear what you said.

The effects of blindness are perceived by sighted people as dramatic and traumatic, but the effects of deafness are often underestimated and dismissed as negligible. Helen Keller, who was both blind and deaf, used to say that while blindness cut her off from things, deafness cut her off from people. Often deafness is seen as one of the minor irritations of the ageing process, rather than as a disability in its own right.

> Deafness is of course very much a nuisance and its disadvantages are severe. The deaf and blind Helen Keller said that she found deafness worse than blindness.
>
> Wright, 1969

> If you prick us, do we not bleed?
>
> Shakespeare, *The Merchant of Venice*

The one disability that people frequently make jokes about is deafness. Not many people would laugh at a blind person who walked into a lamp post; or mock a wheelchair user who was unable to negotiate a staircase – but jokes about deaf people by hearing people are both frequent and unkind. (Jokes about deafness by deaf people are a different story and are usually greatly enjoyed.) When grandmother has problems coping, talking to the girl on the check-out at the supermarket, this may raise a smile on your part (or more likely, a sense of exasperation and irritation with your grandmother). If grandmother was using a walking stick and was unable to negotiate the flight of six stairs into the supermarket, you would be very indignant on her behalf and probably start a campaign to get a ramp installed. The people who usually campaign for loop systems for hearing aid users are hard of hearing people themselves! (Another interesting point: most ramps are in working order, most loop systems in public places may well be in working order but are often not switched on.)

Deafness is also used as an insult. When someone fails to respond as quickly as it is felt they should. how often do people angrily say 'Are you deaf? I've asked you three times!' Does anyone ever stop to think that they might be?

Courtesy, consideration and communication

What is the main problem facing hard of hearing people? Communication. There may be hard of hearing people who miss birdsong. There may be hard of hearing people who use their ears in their work, such as musicians, who miss these specialised sounds. There are those who have enjoyable hobbies where they miss the accompanying sound – a fisherman may miss the sound of water lapping – but on the whole what gives most deaf people problems most of the time is hearing, or rather not hearing, the human voice. Beethoven sums this up very well – we want to be able to communicate with other people, everyone does (deaf and hearing) but this very want is the source of many of our problems.

> Though endowed with a passionate and lively temperament and even fond of the distractions offered by society I was soon obliged to seclude myself and live in solitude. If at times I decided to ignore my infirmity, alas! how cruelly was I then driven back by the intensified sad experience of my poor hearing. Yet I could not bring myself to say to people: 'Speak up, shout, for I am deaf.'
>
> Van Beethoven, L. 'Heiligenstadt Testament' quoted in Grant, 1987

Communication between hearing and hard of hearing people is a two-way thing. It takes two to tango and two to communicate. Hearing people often behave as if the responsibility for communication always lies with the hard of hearing person. The analogy often drawn is that of a wheelchair user. If you have a friend who is a wheelchair user, you would not ask them to run upstairs and fetch you something. Yet hearing people expect hard of hearing people to be able to hear perfectly in noisy situations and are very affronted when they cannot. If hard of hearing people can go to the trouble of wearing their hearing aids or implants and learning to lipread, the least hearing people can do is to try and meet them halfway.

How can communication be made more comfortable for hard of hearing people? When engaged in conversation with a hard of hearing person, it is very helpful if you:

◆ attract the attention of the person you wish to speak to;
◆ face the person you are talking to;
◆ sit or stand with the light on your face;
◆ sit if the person you are talking to is sitting, stand if they are standing;
◆ turn off any background noise, such as the television;
◆ repeat a sentence when asked;
◆ do not say one word at a time and speak with normal phrasing – it is easier to

lipread phrases than words because there is more context;

- ◆ rephrase what you have just said – sometimes a different choice of words can be easier to lipread;
- ◆ write things down when necessary;
- ◆ speak clearly and a little slower than usual;
- ◆ do not speak into a person's ear or hearing aid – if you do that they cannot lipread you at the same time;
- ◆ keep a moustache or beard well trimmed so that it does not obscure your lips – people with full moustaches and beards can be difficult to lipread;
- ◆ introduce the topic you are talking about (not 'There were lots of people there, considering the weather' but 'Would you like to hear about my son Steven's wedding?')
- ◆ refrain from speaking while eating or drinking, or chewing gum;
- ◆ avoid shouting – shouting distorts the shape of the mouth, and loud sounds are picked up by hearing aids, amplified and can be extremely uncomfortable;
- ◆ communicate with the person themselves – do not use their hearing friend or relative as an interpreter! Do not say 'Would Susan like a cup of tea?', ask Susan herself!
- ◆ avoid pained or exasperated facial expressions and body language;
- ◆ avoid jokes about hearing loss;
- ◆ do not ignore any deaf people present.

You will observe that none of these things costs money and none of them requires a university degree in Deaf Studies – merely a little time and effort. It is ironic that British Sign Language classes are becoming so popular amongst hearing people who want to communicate with deaf people. BSL is a wonderful language but it takes time, patience and money to learn. There are about 70,000 deaf people who use BSL. There are over 8 million people who are hard of hearing. They do not use BSL. Basic communication skills are easy and quick to learn – and free.

Include rather than exclude

One of the hardest things to experience is the feeling of being left out. We all know how that feels. Remember when you were at school, when the other children excluded you from their game? Remember when you were not picked for the football team? Remember when your sister and her friends were whispering secrets that they would not share with you? Whether it is the children in the playground refusing to play, or a parliamentary candidate not getting elected, we all hate to be excluded. If you have a hard of hearing friend, relative or colleague, make an effort to include them in your conversations. If you wish to keep your deaf friends please avoid such remarks as these:

> **'I'll tell you later.'** How many people remember later?
> **'It doesn't matter.'** Yes it does, or you would not have said it.
> **'It wasn't funny anyway.'** So in that case, why is everyone laughing? Are they laughing at me?

Sometimes the hearing person may just be tired or have a headache. However, what the deaf person may feel that the hearing person in such situations is saying is 'I can't be bothered.' 'You are not important enough for me to make an effort on your behalf.' 'Your deafness embarrasses me.'

Deaf not daft

Hard of hearing people are just people like you.

If I can live with this dilemma
It doesn't seem too much
To ask others
To recognise
How I'm different
But very ordinary
Ordinary and very different

      Maria Jastzebska, 'The Horns of My Dilemma', in Keith (ed.) *Mustn't Grumble*

The only difference between hearing people and hard of hearing people is that hard of hearing people's ears do not work as well as they once did. There is nothing, repeat nothing, wrong with their brains. Even if they cannot always hear what is said, they can read facial expressions and body language. They know when people find them irritating, boring or exasperating. The shrug, the smile, the raised eyebrows, the rolling eyes, the exaggerated sighs, the curled lip – shall we go on? These signs of annoyance can make the situation worse. When a hard of hearing person sees such signs they become upset, and when they become upset it is more difficult for them to hear. Why? Lipreading and listening require a great deal of concentration. It is difficult to concentrate when stressed or unhappy.

Poor communication → misunderstanding → irritation → stress → further poor communication → more stress

If you find hearing loss irritating, can you imagine what it is like for someone who is deaf? Please do not blame them for their deafness. Strange though it may seem, they did not become deaf deliberately with the intention of annoying you! Samuel Johnson, the 18th century writer famous for compiling the first English dictionary, did not find other people's deafness irritating – he called deafness 'one of the most desperate of human calamities'.[2] But then, Dr Johnson was a man who loved to talk and who loved to hear others talk. He was also a man of great intelligence and imagination and realised what it must be like to be cut off from conversation with others.

Notes
1 RNID, 2003
2 Johnson, Samuel. *Journey to the Western Islands of Scotland.* Dr Johnson had just visited a school for deaf children in Edinburgh and been very impressed by the high standard of their education.

Communication handout

Good communication is really just good manners and commonsense. Here are a few guidelines to help you. You and your deaf friends or relatives, will be able to add other points to the list.

- Attract the attention of the person you wish to speak to.
- Face the person you are talking to.
- Sit or stand with the light on your face.
- Sit if the person you are talking to is sitting, stand if they are standing.
- Turn off any background noise, such as the television.
- Repeat a sentence when asked.
- Rephrase what you have just said. Sometimes a different choice of words can be easier to lipread.
- Write things down when necessary.
- Speak clearly and a little slower than usual.
- Introduce the topic you are talking about. Not, 'There were lots of people there, considering the weather.' But: 'Would you like to hear about my son Steven's wedding?'
- Refrain from speaking while eating or drinking, or chewing gum.
- Avoid shouting. Shouting distorts the shape of the mouth and loud sounds are picked up by hearing aids, amplified and can be extremely uncomfortable.
- Please communicate with the person themselves. Do not use their hearing friend or relative as an interpreter! Do not say, 'Would Susan like a cup of tea?' Ask Susan herself!
- Please avoid:
  - pained or exasperated facial expressions and body language;
  - jokes about hearing loss;
  - ignoring any deaf people who are present.
- If you wish to keep your deaf friends, try not to say any of the following:
  - **'I'll tell you later.'** How many people remember later?
  - **'It doesn't matter.'** Yes it does, or you would not have said it.
  - **'It wasn't funny anyway.'** So in that case, why is everyone laughing? Are they laughing at me?

Appendix 1

Useful addresses

Please remember that the names and details of organisations do alter from time to time. Although this list was up to date at the time of going to press, there may have been changes already!

Age Concern
1268 London Road
London SW16 4ER
Tel: 020 8765 7200
Fax: 020 8765 7211
Website: www.ageconcern.org.uk

Association of Lipspeakers (ALS)
Information Office
5 Furlong Close
Upper Tean
Stoke-on-Trent ST10 4LB
Tel: 01538 722482
Fax/textphone: 01538 722442
Email: information@lipspeaking.co.uk
Website: www.lipspeaking.co.uk

Association of Teachers of Lipreading to Adults (ATLA)
Westwood Park
London Road
Little Horkesley
Colchester CO6 4BS
Email: ATLA@lipreading.org.uk
Website: www.lipreading.org.uk

Audio Medical Devices Ltd
343 Eden Park Avenue
Beckenham BR3 3JN
Tel: 020 8663 0760
Fax: 020 8663 0163
Email: info@audimed.com
Website: www.audimed.com

Better Hearing
2B Lynwood Close
Harrow HA2 9PR
Tel: 07830 179084/07714 394723
Fax: 020 8248 1179
Email: advice@betterhearing.co.uk
Website: www.betterhearing.co,

Bio-Acoustics
Mead House
Spring Place
Luton LU1 5DF
Tel: 01582 431000
Text: 01582 481411
Website: www.BioAcoustics.com

British Cochlear Implant Group
Email: jane.martin@bradfordhospitalnhs.uk
Website: www.bcig.org

British Deaf Association
1–3 Worship Street
London EC2A 2AB
Tel: 0870 770 3300
Fax: 020 7588 3527
Email: helpline@bda.org.uk
Email: helpline@signcommunity.org.uk
Website: www.britishdeafassociation.org.uk
Website: www.signcommunity.org.uk

British Tinnitus Association
Ground Floor Unit 5
Acorn Business Park
Woodseats Close
Sheffield S8 OTB
Tel: 0800 018 0527
Text: 0114 258 5694
Fax: 0114 258 2279
Email: info@tinnitus.org.uk
Website: www.tinnitus.org.uk

BT Age and Disability
BT Age & Disability Action
PP38/15
Britannia Road
Waltham Cross EN8 7NR
Tel: 0800 800 150
Fax: 01332 822839
Email: disability@bt.com
Website: www.shop.bt.com

City Lit Centre for Deaf People
Keeley Street
Covent Garden
London WC2B 4BA
Tel: 020 7242 9872
Fax: 020 7492 2735
Website: www.citylit.ac.uk

Connevans Limited
54 Albert Road North
Reigate RH2 9YR
Tel: 01737 247571

Text: 01737 243134
Fax: 01737 223475
Email: info@connevans.com
Website: www.connevans.com

The Council for the Advancement of Communication with Deaf People (CACDP)
Durham University Science Park Block 4
Stockton Road
Durham DH1 3UZ
Tel: 0191 383 1155
Text: 0191 383 7915
Fax: 0191 383 7914
Email: durham@cacdp.org.uk
Website: www.cacdp.org.uk

Cued Speech Association
9 Duke Street
Dartmouth TQ6 9PY
Tel/Text: 01803 832784
Fax: 01803 835311
Email: info@cuedspeech.co.uk
Website: www.cuedspeech.co.uk

Deafblind UK
John and Lucille van Geest Place
Cygnet Road
Hampton
Peterborough PE7 8FD
Tel/Text: 01733 358100
Fax: 01733 358356
Email: info@deafblind.org.uk
Website: www.deafblind.org.uk

Deafplus
Empire Court
Albert Street
Redditch B97 4DA
Tel/Text: 01527 592080
Fax: 01527 69000
Website: www.deafplus.org

Deafworks
59 Banner Street
London EC1Y 8PX
Tel: 020 7689 0033
Text: 020 7689 1048
Fax: 020 7689 1049
Email: general@deafworks.co.uk
Website: www.deafworks.co.uk

Deafness Research Trust
330–332 Gray's Inn Road
London WC1X 8DA
Tel: 020 7833 1733

Text: 020 7915 1412
Fax: 020 7278 0404
Email: info@defeatingdeafness.org
Website: www.defeatingdeafness.org

Disability Rights Commission (DRC)
DRC Helpline
FREEPOST MIDO 2164
Stratford upon Avon CV37 9BR
Tel: 08457 622 633
Text: 08457 622 644
Fax: 08457 778 878
Website: www.drc-gb.org

Enabling Through Sound And Music (ETSAM)
3 Thornton Grove
Morecambe LA4 5PU
Tel: 01524 427919/07811 962466
Email: info@ETSAM.org.uk
Website: www.ETSAM.org.uk

Forest Books
The New Building
Ellwood Road
Milkwall
Coleford GL16 7LE
Tel/Text: 01594 833858
Video 01594 810637
Fax: 01594 833446
Email: forest@forestbooks.com
Website: www.ForestBooks.com

Hearing Concern
95 Gray's Inn Road
London WC1X 8TX
Tel: 020 7440 9871
Fax/Text: 020 7440 9872
Email: info@hearingconcern.org.uk
Website: www.hearingconcern.org.uk

Hearing Dogs for Deaf People
The Grange
Wycombe Road
Saunderton
Princes Risborough HP27 9NS
Tel/Text: 01844 348100
Fax: 01844 348101
Email: info@hearing-dogs.co.uk
Website: www.hearing-dogs.co.uk

Jewish Deaf Association
Julius Newman House
Woodside Park Road
Off High Road
North Finchley

London N12 8RP
Tel: 020 8446 0502
Text: 020 8446 4037
Fax: 020 8445 7451
Email: mail@jda.dircon.co.uk
Website: www.jewishdeaf.org.uk

LINK Centre for Deafened People
19 Hartfield Road
Eastbourne BN21 2AR
Tel: 01323 638230
Text: 01323 739998
Fax: 01323 642968
Email: info@linkdp.org
Website: www.linkcentre.org

MAGIC (Museums and Galleries in the Capital)
c/o The British Museum
Education Department
London WC1B 3DG
Fax: 020 7323 8855
Email: info@magicdeaf.org.uk
Website: www.magicdeaf.org.uk/about/home.asp

Ménière's Society
The Rookery
Surrey Hills Business Park
Wotton
Dorking RH5 6QT
Tel: 01306 876883
Fax: 01306 876057
Email: info@menieres.org.uk
Website: www.menieres.co.uk

National Association for Deafened People (NADP)
PO Box 50
Amersham HP6 6XB
Tel: 01227 379538
Text: 01227 762879
Fax: 01227 379538
Email: enquiries@nadp.org.uk
Website: www.nadp.org.uk

National Cochlear Implant Users Association
Jane Riches
Administrator NCIU
PO Box 260
High Wycombe HPII IFA
Email: enquiries@nciua.demon.co.uk
Website: www.nciua.demon.co.uk

National Deaf Children's Society (NDCS)
15 Dufferin Street
London EC1Y 8UR
Tel: 020 7490 8656

Fax: 020 7251 5020
Email: helpline@ndcs.org.uk
Website: www.ndcs.org.uk

National Subtitling Library for Deaf People
3rd Floor Victoria Mill
Andrew Street
Compstall
Stockport SK6 1DJ
Tel: 0161 449 9650
Email: members@nsldp.freeserve.co.uk
Website: www.la-hq.org.uk

Neurofibromatosis Association UK
Quayside House
38 High Street
Kingston-on-Thames KT1 1HL
Tel: 020 8439
Text: 020 8481 0492
Fax: 020 8439 1200
Email: info@nfauk.org
Website: www.nfauk.org

Open Ears (Formerly the Hard of Hearing Christian Fellowship)
11 York Avenue
New Milton BH25 6BT
Email: admin@openears.org.uk

Royal Association for Deaf People (RAD)
Walsingham Road
Colchester CO2 7BP
Tel: 01206 509509
Fax: 01206 769755
Email: info@royaldeaf.org.uk
Website: www.royaldeaf.org.uk

Royal National Institute for Deaf People RNID
19–23 Featherstone Street
London EC1Y 8SL
Tel: 0808 808 0123
Text: 0808 808 9000
Fax: 020 7296 8199
Email: informationline@rnid.org.uk
Website: www.rnid.org.uk

Sarabec
15 High Force Road
Middlesbrough TS2 1RH
Tel: 01642 247789
Text: 01642 251310
Fax: 01642 230 827
Email: mail@sarabec.co.uk
Website: www.sarabec.com

SENSE (The National Deafblind Association)
11–13 Clifton Terrace
Finsbury Park
London N4 3SR
Tel: 020 7272 7774
Text: 020 7272 9648
Fax: 020 7272 6012
Email: enquiries@sense.org.uk
Website: www.sense.org.uk

SHAPE (Access to the Arts)
LVS Resource Centre
356 Holloway Road
London N7 6PA
Tel: 020 7619 6160
Email: info@shapearts.org.uk
Website: www.shapearts.org.uk

Signed Performances In Theatre (SPIT)
1 Stobart Avenue
Manchester M25 0AJ
Tel: 0161 773 1715
Email: sarah@spit.org.uk

Sound Advantage RNID
1 Haddonbrook Business Centre
Orton Southgate
Peterborough PE2 6YX
Tel: 0870 789 8855
Text: 01733 238020
Fax: 0870 789 8822
Email: solutions@rnid.org.uk
Website: www.rnidshop.com

Stagetext
12th Floor York House
Empire Way
Wembley
London HA9 OPA
Tell 020 8903 5566
Email: enquiries@stagetext.org
Website: www.stagetext.org

Subtitles at Your Local Cinema
Website: www.yourlocalcinema.com/index.html

Typetalk
PO Box 284
Liverpool L69 3UZ
Tel: 0151 709 9494
Email: helpline@rnid-typetalk.org.uk
Website: www.rnid-typetalk.org.uk

UK Council On Deafness (UKCOD)
Westwood Park
London Road

Little Horkesley
Colchester CO6 4BS
Tel: 01206 274075
Text: 01206 274076
Fax: 01206 274077
Email: info@deafcouncil.org.uk
Website: www.deafcouncil.org.uk

Usher Life
Email: contact@usherlife.co.uk
Website: www.usherlife.co.uk

Appendix 2

Further reading

General

Dempster D and J (eds). *Daily Telegraph: A Quiet Pint: a guide to pubs with no piped music.* London: Aurum Press Ltd, 2004.

Dunmore K, Riddiford G, Tait V. *Understanding Tinnitus: living with the noises in your ears or in your head.* Coleford: Forest Books for RNID, 2003.

Graham J, Martin M (eds). *Ballantyne's Deafness,* 6th Edition. Chichester: Wiley, 2001.

Kubler-Ross E. *On Death and Dying.* New York: Scribner's, 1997.

Morris, J. *Pride Against Prejudice.* London: The Women's Press Ltd, 1991.

Polsdorfer, JR. *Gale Encyclopaedia of Medicine: Hearing Loss. Volume 3.* Stamford, Conn: Thomson Gale, 2002.

RNID. *Facts and Figures on Deafness and Tinnitus,* January 2003.

Stone, Howard E 'Rocky'. *An Invisible Condition: the human side of hearing loss.* Pennsylvania: SHHH Publications.

Yardley, L. *Vertigo and Dizziness.* London: Routledge, 1994.

Autobiographical

Ashley, Jack. *Acts of Defiance.* London: Reinhardt Books, 1994.

Cartagena, Teresa de. *The Writings of Teresa de Cartagena,* trans. Dayle Seidenspinner-Nuñez. *The Writings of the Library of Medieval Women series.* (ed. Jane Chance). Woodbridge, Suffolk, and Rochester, New York: Boydell & Brewer, 1998.

Glennie, Evelyn. *Good Vibrations.* London: Hutchinson, 1990.

Golan, Lew. *Reading Between The Lips: A totally deaf man makes it in the mainstream.* Chicago: Bonus Books, 1995.

Keller, Helen. *The Story of My Life.* New York: American Foundation for the Blind, 2003.

Locke, Angela and Harmer, Jenny. *Hearing Dog: the story of Jennie and Connie.* London: Souvenir Press Ltd, 1997.

Morrey, Will. *Seeing is Hearing: reflections on being deafened.* Bangor: University of Wales, 1994.

Romoff, Arlene. *Hear Again: back to life with a cochlear implant.* New York: Sterling Publishing, 2002.

Simmons, Michael. *Hearing Loss: from stigma to strategy.* London: Peter Owen Publishers, 2004.

Taylor G, Bishop J. *Being deaf: the experience of deafness.* London: Pinter publishers, 1991.

Wright, David. *Deafness: an autobiography.* London: Mandarin, 1969.

Fiction

Batson T, Bergman U (eds). *Angels and Outcasts: an anthology of deaf characters in literature.* Washington DC: Gallaudet College Press, 1973.

Dexter, Colin. *The Silent World of Nicholas Quinn.* London: Pan Books, 1978.

Gallagher B. *The Feng-Shui Junkie.* London: Orion Books, 2000.

Grant, Brian (ed.). *The Quiet Ear: deafness in literature.* London: Deutsch, 1987.

Itani, Frances. *Deafening.* London: Sceptre, 2004.

Jepson J (ed.). *No Walls of Stone: an anthology of literature by deaf and hard of hearing writer.* Washington DC: Gallaudet, 1997

Kenyon D. 'Reaction–interaction' in L Keith, ed. *Mustn't Grumble: writing by disabled women.* London: The Women's Press, 1994.

McCullers, Carson. *The Heart is a Lonely Hunter.* London: Penguin Books, 2001.

Medoff, Mark. *Children of a Lesser God.* Charlbury, Oxon: Amber Lane Press, 1996.

Seth, Vikram. *An Equal Music.* London: BCA, 1999.

Suchet, John. *The Last Master: a fictional biography of Ludwig van Beethoven* (3 volumes). London: Time Warner Paperbacks, 1996–8.

Poetry

Murray, Les A. 'Hearing Impairment' in *Learning Human: Selected Poems.* New York: Farrar, Straus & Giroux, 2000.

Traherne, Thomas. *Centuries, Poems, and Thanksgivings.* (Ed. HM Margoliouth). 2 vols. London: Oxford UP, 1958.

Lipreading and communication tactics

Campbell R, Dodd B, Burnham D (eds). *Hearing by Eye II: advances in the psychology of speechreading and auditory-visual speech.* London: Taylor and Francis, 1998.

Council for the Advancement of Communication with Deaf People. *Communication Tactics* (video) from CACDP with subtitles or BSL subtitles.

Council for the Advancement of Communication with Deaf People. *Fingerspelling for Lipreaders* (video) from CACDP.

Kaplan H, Bally SJ, Garretson C. *Speechreading: a way to improve understanding.* Washington DC: Gallaudet Press,1995.

Mansfield, J. *To Hear or Not to Hear/I'm Only Deaf* (video). Coleford: Forest Books.

Nitchie, EB. *Lip-reading principles and practice: a handbook for teachers and for self instruction.* Whitefish, MT: Kessinger Publishing [Lightning Source UK Ltd], 2004.

Sherren P, Martin C. *Look Hear: introduction to lipreading* (video) from Lip Service. Coleford: Forest Books, 1989.

Speech Tutor: a lipreading and pronunciation aid (CD ROM). Coleford: Forest Books, 2003.

Woods, JC. *Watch This Face.* RNID via Forest Books (Coleford), 2001.

Self-help

Bagshaw, Caroline. *The Hard of Hearing Handbook.* London: Imperia Books, 1994.

'Bridging the communication gap. The relationship between deaf grandparents and their grandchildren.' *Conference – Self Help for the Hard of Hearing Congress,* San Diego, USA, June 1995.

Buzan, Tony. *Head First.* London: Harper Collins Publishers, 2000.

Buzan, Tony. *Use Your Head.* London: BBC Books, 1997.

Davies, Rodney. *How to Read Faces.* London: The Aquarian Press/Thorson's, 1989.

Dugan, Marcia B. *Living with Hearing Loss.* Washington DC: Gallaudet University Press, 2003.

Dunmore K, Riddiford G, Tait V. *Understanding Tinnitus: living with the noises in your ears or in your head.* Coleford: Forest Books for RNID, 2003.

McCall, Rosemary. *Hearing Loss? A guide to self-help.* London: Robert Hale Ltd, 1991.

National Association of Deafened People. *Deaf People Can.* Amersham: NADP, 1992.

Stenross, Barbara. *Missed Connections: hard of hearing in a hearing world.* Philadelphia: Temple University Press, 1999.

Stone, Carole *'Networking': the art of making friends.* London: Ebury Press, 2000.

Thomsett K, Nickerson E. *Missing Words: family handbook on adult hearing loss.* Washington DC: Gallaudet University Press, 1997.

Whiteside, Robert. *Face Language.* Hollywood, FL: Frederick Fell Publishers, 1998.

Psychology and deafness

Harvey MA. *Listen With The Heart.* Chicago: Independent Publishers Group, 2001.

Harvey MA. *Odyssey of Hearing Loss.* San Diego: Dawn Sign Press, 1998.

Vernon M, Andrews SF. *Psychology of Deafness: understanding deaf and hard of hearing people.* Harlow: Longman Group UK, 1990.

Explaining deafness

Freeland, Andrew. *Deafness: the facts.* Oxford: OUP, 1989.

Lysons, Kenneth. *Understanding Hearing Loss.* London: Jessica Kingsley Publishers, 1995.

Academic

Gregory S, Hartley GM. *Constructing Deafness.* London: Pinter Publishers, 1991.

Jones L, Kyle J, Wood P. *Words Apart.* London: Tavistock Publications, 1987.

Morgan-Jones, Ruth. *Hearing Differently: the impact of hearing impairment on family life.* London: Whurr Publishers, 2001.

Ree, Jonathan. *I See A Voice: deafness, language and the senses – a philosophical history.* New York: Henry Holt and Co., 1999.

Weston, Mark. *Working Without Hearing.* Amersham: National Association for Deafened People (and The Link Centre), 2001.

Woodcock K, Aguayo M. *Deafened People: adjustment and support.* Toronto: University of Toronto Press, 2000.

Appendix 3

Glossary

Here are some definitions of words and phrases found in this book.

Access to Work Scheme This is a government scheme that enables people with disabilities to continue working or to find work if they are unemployed. Financial help may be available for such things as buying specialist equipment (for example a text telephone); training and communication support during job interviews (for example a BSL interpreter or lipspeaker). Ask at your local Job Centre where a special officer is employed to advise people about this scheme.

Acoustic neuroma A benign tumour on the auditory nerve, usually slow growing.

Acoustics The science of sound.

Amplified telephone A telephone that has a volume control to amplify the voice of the person speaking at the other end. Amplified telephones often have an extra loud bell, a flashing light and a loop system. (See Appendix 1 Useful Addresses for the names of firms who stock special equipment. British Telecom sells amplified telephones.)

Amplifier Any device that increases the incoming signal from a sound source.

Audiogram A diagram in the form of a graph, representing a person's level of hearing. The x axis represents frequency and the y axis represents volume.

Audiologist Audiologists are qualified to perform diagnostic testing on people suspected of having hearing loss, balance disorders and tinnitus. Audiologists are also trained to fit and repair hearing aids. Audiology is now a graduate profession and NHS audiologists have voluntary registration at present. They will shortly have compulsory state registration.

Audiology The study of ears and hearing. The word comes from the Latin *audire* – to hear.

Audiology Unit/Department The hospital department dealing with hearing loss, tinnitus and balance. It can also be called a Hearing Centre.

Auditory nerve The nerve of hearing, also known as the VIIIth nerve. It transmits signals from the cochlea in the ear to the brain.

Auditory training To improve your residual hearing a Hearing Therapist will sometimes suggest auditory training. This means practising the sounds you have problems with by means of carefully constructed listening exercises.

Auditory tube This is sometimes known as the Eustachian tube and connects the middle ear to the back of the nose. It helps to balance the pressure inside the ear with the pressure outside.

Balance rehabilitation Balance retraining works on the basis that practising simple eye and body movements improves the balance. It also involves counselling and support and is normally very successful.

British Sign Language This is Sign Language used by the Deaf Community in Britain. BSL has its own grammar, syntax and vocabulary, just as spoken languages do. Like spoken English, it has its own regional variations.

Cerumen Wax found in the ear canal. Its function is to keep the outer ear clean. On no account should you attempt to remove it using a cotton bud.

Closed question See also *Open Question*. A closed question is one to which the answer can only be, 'Yes', or 'No'. For example, 'Is it raining?'

Cochlea The cochlea is in the inner ear and is shaped like a shell. On one side of it are the ossicles and on the other side is the auditory nerve. The cochlea's job is to transmit sound vibration into electrical impulses.

Cochlear implant A cochlear implant is a device that artificially stimulates the auditory nerve by means of an electrode that has been surgically inserted into the cochlea. It *does not* 'cure' deafness and should rather be thought of as a kind of sophisticated hearing aid. An implant can improve hearing but only in people whose hearing loss is cochlear in origin. The amount of improvement it gives varies.

Communication tactics Communication tactics involve using a mixture of common sense and a knowledge of basic acoustics together with lipreading and residual hearing in order to communicate. Deaf people also use other senses, such as vision, or touch, or smell to compensate for what they cannot hear.

Conductive deafness Conductive deafness is caused by a problem with the outer or middle ear, i.e. with the mechanical part of the ear (the pinna, the ear canal, or the ossicles). Conductive deafness makes things sound very quiet. Some people with conductive deafness hear better in background noise and usually find hearing aids very helpful. The ability of people with conductive deafness to hear better in background noise is known as paracusia willisiana.

Deaf (with a capital D) Deaf people are members of the Deaf Community. They were usually born Deaf and use BSL as their preferred method of communication. The difference between Deaf and deaf people is a linguistic and cultural one.

deaf (with a small d) People who lose all, or part, of their hearing in later life are known as deaf people. They are also known as hearing impaired or hard of hearing people. Their preferred method of communication is usually speech and lipreading. The difference between deaf and Deaf people is a linguistic and cultural one.

Deaf Awareness Deaf Awareness consists of an understanding of the rights of people with disabilities; an appreciation of some of the problems facing people with hearing loss; a knowledge of communication tactics and a willingness to empower people with hearing loss so that they have equal access.

Decibel (dB) Decibels are used to measure how loud a sound is. A decibel is one tenth of a bel (named after Alexander Graham Bell).

Dental audition An obsolete name for lipreading.

Disability Hearing loss is an impairment. To be unable to use an ordinary telephone because of one's hearing loss is a disability. To be prevented from communication with a bank or business, for example, because they do not have a textphone, email or fax is to be handicapped. People are not handicapped unless society handicaps them.

Disability Discrimination Act (DDA) The DDA means that disabled people have rights, which are now enshrined in law, e.g. the right to such things as equal access to education, employment, services, leisure activities and public transport. Service providers, for example, colleges and businesses, have responsibilities, such as providing loop systems, ramps, written information in Braille, etc.

Door beacon An alerting device that responds to a knock on a door.

Ear canal (external auditory meatus) The tube-shaped part of the ear that joins the pinna to the eardrum. It channels and amplifies sound.

Eardrum Also known as the tympanic membrane. The eardrum is the flexible piece of skin that separates the ear canal from the ossicles. It is possible to see the tip of the ossicles through a healthy eardrum.

Ear mould The ear mould is the part of a behind-the-ear hearing aid that fits inside the ear (as opposed to the part that goes behind the ear). It is an important part of the hearing aid and it is vital that it fits properly. Ear moulds have to be custom made, as each person's ears are a different shape.

ENT/Head and Neck Ear Nose and Throat or Head and Neck Department. Hospitals have separate departments to deal with specific conditions or parts of the body. This is partly because hospital doctors specialise. An Ear Nose and Throat Department does just that – it deals with all problems related to the ear, nose or throat. Audiology is managed by the ENT Department.

Eustachian tube See *Auditory tube*. The Eustachian tube is named after the famous Italian anatomist, Bartolomeo Eustachio (approx. 1510–1574) who first described the Eustachian tube in detail.

Exostosis (plural – exostoses) Sometimes known as osteoma, these are small, bony growths in the ear canal. They are most commonly found in the ears of keen swimmers.

External auditory meatus See *Ear canal*.

Hearing aid management This may include such things as making sure that the hearing aid is comfortable; the hearing aid user knows how to clean the ear mould of the aid; the deaf person has been instructed in basic communication tactics; and that counselling is available.

Hearing Therapist A Hearing Therapist is a trained professional who empowers people who have lost their hearing as adults to adjust to their hearing loss. Hearing therapy involves such things as: auditory training, balance retraining, communication tactics, counselling, special equipment (sometimes called environmental aids), teaching lipreading and tinnitus management. Hearing therapy is now a graduate profession and will shortly have compulsory state registration.

Incus The second bone of the ossicular chain. It is so called because it is anvil shaped. *Incus* is the Latin word for 'anvil'.

Infrared device A device commonly used in public places, such as theatres, to enhance the hearing. The hard of hearing or deaf person wears a neckloop and their hearing aids (on T) or a headset without their hearing aids. This device picks up and amplifies sound from the speaker and relays it to the listener using infrared rays.

Inner ear The inner ear consists of the cochlea and the auditory nerve associated with the organ of balance and vestibular nerve. The two nerves join on their way to the brain to form the eighth nerve.

Labial augury An obsolete term for lipreading.

Labiology An obsolete term for lipreading.

Labiomancy An obsolete term for lipreading.

Language Service Professional (LSP) Formerly called a Human Aid to Communication (HAC). An LSP is a specially trained professional who facilitates communication between deaf and hearing people. LSPs include professionals such as Sign Language Interpreters, lipspeakers, deafblind communicators and palantypists.

Lipreading The ability to comprehend a speaker by watching the movements of their lips, their facial expression and their body language.

Lipspeaker A human aid to communication (or Language Service Professional). One who relays what someone has just said to a deaf person using the movements of their lips only without voice. They also use facial expression, gesture and fingerspelling.

Loop system Induction loops are often found in public buildings, such as stations, shops and theatres. Loop systems are also available for use in the home (See Appendix 1 Useful Addresses for a list of firms that supply special equipment. Social services often loan equipment for the home. Ask your local Social Services Department if they provide this service.) Since a loop transfers sound directly from the source of the sound to the hearing aid, it cuts out background noise. Sound can be amplified either by using the volume control on your hearing aid or the volume control on the loop system itself. Loop systems can be used only with hearing aids that have a loop switch (often marked with a 'T'). NHS hearing aids have a loop switch but not all private hearing aids do.

Malleus The first bone of the ossicles. The word is the Latin word for 'hammer'.

Ménière's disease No one knows for certain what causes the onset of Ménière's disease. It is characterised by episodes of vertigo, fullness in the ear, fluctuating nerve deafness and roaring tinnitus. It was first described by a French doctor called Prosper Ménière(1799–1862).

Middle ear The middle ear contains the ossicles, three small bones, which transmit sound vibrations from the eardrum to the cochlea.

Myringoplasty The name given to an operation to repair a hole (perforation) in the eardrum by patching it with a graft.

Nasopharynx The nasopharynx joins the nose and throat together. The Eustachian tube opens into the nasopharynx.

National Health Service (NHS) 1948 saw the introduction of the National Health Service. The NHS seeks to provide a cradle to the grave health service for everyone. It is paid for out of taxation. It is not a charity but an entitlement.

Noise-induced hearing loss (NIHL) Noise-induced hearing loss is caused by repeated exposure to excessive noise (80–90 dB and over). The hearing loss caused is a type of sensorineural (nerve) deafness and is not reversible. Loud noise can also cause tinnitus. People who are regularly exposed to loud noise should use some form of ear protection if they wish to preserve their hearing.

Note-taker A human aid to communication. Someone who takes notes for a deaf or hard of hearing person, e.g. during a lecture or meeting. Note-taking is a skilled job and note-takers are specially trained and qualified.

Occular audition An obsolete term for lipreading.

Open question See also *Closed question*. An open question is one to which the answer could be almost anything, e.g. 'What's the weather like out?' or 'What's your favourite meal?'

Oral audition An obsolete term for lipreading.

Ossicles A chain of three small bones in the middle ear, the malleus, the incus and the stapes, which transmit sound from the eardrum to the cochlea.

Osteoma (plural – osteomata) See *Exostosis*.

Otalgia Earache. It can be caused, not only by problems with the ear, but also by problems with the teeth, jaw, neck and throat.

Otitis externa Inflammation or infection of the ear canal.

Otitis media Inflammation or infection of the middle ear.

Ototoxic drugs Medication that may have a detrimental effect on the hearing and/or tinnitus. The main groups of ototoxic drugs are: aminoglycoside antibiotics (e.g. streptomycin.); some other antibiotics (e.g. erythromycin.); loop diuretics (e.g. frusemide); salicylates (e.g. aspirin); quinine derivatives. Some drugs affect people's hearing or tinnitus only if the doses are large enough. Some drugs have only a temporary effect. Always consult your doctor if you are worried about your medication.

Outer ear The visible part of the ear consisting of the pinna and the ear canal. The pinna and one-third of the ear canal are largely made of cartilage.

Palantype A machine used to improve communication for deaf people. A palantypist listens to what is said and types it onto a special keyboard. The keyboard uses a form of shorthand. The transcribed speech is projected onto a screen so that all present can read it.

Perforation A hole, or tear in the eardrum, often self-healing. This can sometimes be repaired by a myringoplasty. Perforations can be caused by infection or trauma.

Personal listening system A hand-held amplifier to increase the incoming volume of sound coming from an individual speaker or the TV.

Pinna (auricle) The pinna is the visible part of the ear and is outside the head. It is stiffened by cartilage and catches sound waves before channelling them down the ear canal.

Presbyacusis A kind of nerve deafness caused by the ageing process. It is the most common cause of hearing loss. The hair-like cells in the cochlea start to deteriorate round about the age of 50. Presbyacusis is gradual.

Recruitment Some people whose hearing loss is caused by a problem with the cochlea, find that sounds can become uncomfortably loud very quickly. This is called recruitment. It seems very odd that deaf people should find some sounds painfully loud – but it is a scientific fact.

Referred pain (synalgia) Pain in one part of the body caused by a problem in another part of the body. For example, trouble with wisdom teeth may cause earache; trouble with the heart may cause a pain in the left arm. Referred pain is caused by the fact that nerve fibres from different parts of the body may enter the same part of the spinal cord. Signals from the nerves are processed in the brain.

Repair strategies Simple things to do when communication breaks down, for example asking someone to repeat what they have said or asking a question or admitting that you have not heard are three examples of repair strategies.

Residual hearing The hearing you have left. This is measured by a pure tone audiogram (PTA) and represented on a chart called an audiogram.

Sensorineural deafness (nerve deafness) Deafness caused by damage to the cochlea or the auditory nerve, for example presbyacusis or noise-induced hearing loss (NIHL). Sensorineural deafness makes sound quieter and indistinct. It becomes difficult to hear in background noise.

Speechreading Another term for lipreading. This is the phrase commonly used by academics who research and write on the subject. It is also the term most commonly used in America.

Speech-to-text reporter A speech-to-text reporter types a visual verbatim account of exactly what is said. The words are projected onto a screen so that everyone who is at the meeting can read them. (An electronic note-taker gives a précis of what has been said.)

STAGETEXT STAGETEXT is used in theatres. It is rather like television subtitles. Whatever the characters say (or sing) appears simultaneously in writing on a screen.

Stapes The third bone of the ossicular chain. It is shaped like a stirrup – the name comes from the Latin word for a stirrup.

Subtitles Used on many television programmes, videos and DVDs, subtitles are the written equivalent of the characters' speech. Sounds are often represented also, e.g. 'traffic noise in the background' or 'scary music'.

Textphone A textphone is a special telephone for deaf people who are unable to hear on either a conventional or an amplified telephone. A textphone has a keyboard and a screen. They type what they wish to communicate using the keyboard. What the caller wishes to communicate to them appears visually on the screen. A textphone can be used to make a call to another textphone or to a conventional telephone. If the call is made between a textphone and a conventional telephone, Typetalk is used.

Tinnitus Noises in the ears or in the head that can usually only be heard by the person who has the tinnitus. Tinnitus is very common; most people with a hearing loss have it. Advice on management is available where needed. It is seldom a symptom of anything unpleasant.

Tinnitus management This enables a person with tinnitus to learn to control or manage it by means of such things as making changes in what they eat and drink, by relaxing regularly, by using sound therapy, and sometimes by the use of a hearing aid or white noise generator. Counselling is also an important part of the process.

Tympanic membrane See also *Eardrum*. The eardrum separates the outer ear from the middle ear.

Typetalk Typetalk is the name given to a system that acts a communicator between a textphone and a conventional telephone. The Typetalk operator reads what the deaf person types into their textphone and speaks the message to the hearing person. The operator hears what the hearing person says and types it into the textphone and sends it to the deaf person. The conversation takes a little longer as a result and for this reason, deaf people who use this service are entitled to have their telephone bills reduced.

> **Deaf person** (types the message into their textphone) → **operator** (reads the message and speaks it to the hearing person → **hearing person** (listens to message and speaks their reply to the operator) → **the operator** (listens to their reply and types it to the deaf person) → **deaf person** (reads the reply).

Vertigo Someone with vertigo feels dizzy as if they are going round and round. (Sometimes they feel as if the ground is sloping away from them.)

Vibrating alarm clock An alarm clock especially designed for deaf and hard of hearing people. It, or a pad attached to it, is placed under the pillow at night. Instead of ringing to alert the sleeper, it vibrates. Very effective! (See Appendix 1 Useful Addresses for the names of firms that supply equipment.)

Visual communication An obsolete term for lipreading.

Visual hearing An obsolete term for lipreading.

Visual listening An obsolete term for lipreading.

Appendix 4

Quiz: Changes that you hope will take place

A person who is talking to you should:
(Now fill in the gaps; the answers are opposite)

1. Check that there is enough _____ to see by.

2. Help by telling you the _____ of the conversation.

3. Allow a little more _____ before moving onto the next sentence.

4. Is willing to speak _____ and repeat or _____ if necessary.

5. Know that _____ is of little help.

6. Remember to _____ you in the conversation.

7. Remember that you need to see their _____ and not mask it.

8. Keep background _____ to a minimum.

9. Not answer for you, but be _____ .

10. Get your _____ before speaking.

11. Speak _____ and not _____ away when speaking.

12. Speak _____ and not gabble.

13. Not speak with their head in _____

14. _____ difficult proper names down.

The answers can be any of the following:

1. Light
2. Subject, gist, nature, topic
3. Time
4. Slowly, clearly/rephrase, write, spell
5. Shouting
6. Include, bring
7. Mouth, face
8. Noise
9. Patient, helpful
10. Attention
11. Clearly, directly, slowly/turn, look
12. Calmly, slowly, clearly
13. With their hand over their mouth, head in their hands, face turned away, head in a different direction, face in the shadow
14. Write

Appendix 5

Suggestions for discussion with tutors

When you meet your tutor or trainer advise them how they can be most supportive of your needs. The following list may be helpful for you to use as guide.

◆ Discuss the Disabled Students Allowance (DSA) and check what financial support you are entitled to.

◆ Discuss the Access to Work scheme, if you are on a work-related training course.

◆ Ask for written information to be available before the start of the course to avoid any misunderstandings.

◆ Request information in black on yellow or white if you have a visual impairment –it provides greater visual contrast and is easier to read.

◆ If you are dyslexic Comic Sans MS font may be easier to read, since it is clear and simple, and **a** and **g** look like their handwritten equivalents.

◆ Ask about visual warning systems such as fire alarms.

◆ Ask if classrooms are clearly signposted to avoid having to ask someone the way.

◆ Ask if other students will have name labels; if not, ask for a list of the names to be prepared, which you can use when you are introduced to a new person. You may find it useful to ask them to point out their name on the list.

◆ Ask if seating can be arranged in a half circle to facilitate lipreading. If this is not possible explain that you would like the teacher to repeat or write questions on the board and explain why.

◆ If you are using a radio aid, explain how it can be best used.

◆ Check if the videos and DVDs will have captions; if not, request an ou line of their content.

◆ Suggest individual tutorials are held in a quiet room with plenty of light.

◆ Ask if a text or mobile phone number will be available for you to leave a message if you are unable to attend a lecture.

◆ Discuss ways that you can be helped generally and give the 'Guidelines for tutors' handout to the person who will be teaching you.

◆ Thank the person for their support.

Appendix 6

Guidelines for tutors teaching students with a hearing loss

◆ Attract the students' attention before you start to speak.

◆ When talking to the students, speak in a clear, slightly louder than normal, voice – clarity is more important than volume. Speak at a moderate pace.

◆ Face the students when speaking. Your expression and lip movements will assist in understanding what you are saying.

◆ Avoid covering your face when you speak.

◆ When talking, do not turn your head or move around the room or distract the students' attention by making unnecessary hand movements.

◆ Avoid talking to students with your back to the light.

◆ Do not talk when your back is towards the class.

◆ Let your face tell a story.

◆ Remember to pause to give the students time to absorb information before carrying straight on.

◆ Use as many visual aids as possible. This will reinforce the students' learning through a medium other than the spoken word. Give them time to take in the content of the visual aid before speaking about it.

◆ Ensure all DVD and video recordings are shown with captions.

◆ Give students a printed version of a PowerPoint presentation.

◆ Make sure that a note pad is available to write down anything that is not understood.

◆ If possible, avoid wearing glasses that have lenses that darken in bright light or are reflective. The students gain a lot from eye contact.

◆ Avoid wearing large or dangling earrings.

◆ Students could experience problems lipreading people with a beard or moustache – therefore, if possible, please trim your beard and/or moustache.

◆ If support workers are present ensure you have a short break every 20 minutes.

◆ If practical, locate a small well-lit room for individual tutorials. It will be helpful for lipreading if chairs are at the same level.

◆ Obtain students' email addresses or mobile phone numbers in the event of a change of teaching arrangements.

◆ **Remember that lipreading is tiring**.

Index

Note to reader
A page number followed by *n* indicates a 'Notes' entry at the end of some chapters.
Use the Glossary on p. 146 for definitions of words.

noise-induced hearing loss (NIHL) 16
notetaking
    electronic 79, 81
    manual 81
    in surgery 102

O

occasions, special *see* special occasions
ossicles 13
    calcium deposits 15
    immobility 15
    problems 14–15
    trauma 14
osteomata 14
otalgia *see* earache
otitis externa *see* infection of ear
otitis media
    chronic suppurative 15
    with effusion 15
otosclerosis 14
ototoxic drugs 16
outer ear 12

P

parotitis, infectious 21
parties 113–114
perception 35
perforation 36
personal space 110
pinna 12
planes 119
planning ahead 100
positivity 34
posture 59
presbyacusis 15, 21, 90
primitive level of sound 63, 65
public announcements, difficulty in hearing 73, 128
'puffer' for hearing aids 70

R

radios 78, 79
    aids 123–124
rambling 120
Ramsdell, Dr 62–63
REACH 93
relationships, helping with 92
relaxation techniques 100
relay services 79
restaurants 101, 104, 114, 115, 121, 126, 127
    abroad 118
rights, entitlement to 43
ringing in ears *see* tinnitus
Rinne test 20
Royal National Institute for Deaf People (RNID),
    Library 51*n*

S

schwannoma, vestibular *see* acoustic neuroma
self-catering holidays 117
Self Help for Hard of Hearing People (SHHH) 34

self-worth 34
semi-circular canals, problems 15
senses, heightening of other 26
sensorineural hearing loss 15–17, 25
ships 119
shopping 26–27, 102–103, 105, 126
sightseeing 120
Sign Language *see* British Sign Language
signal level of sound 63, 65
smiling, as compensating mechanism 27
social skills, gaining 49, 95–97
    see also special occasions
sounds
    electronically produced 73
    frequency 22, 25
    levels of 62–65
    loudness 16
    at parties 113
    reverberation 73
special occasions
    Christmas 101
    parties 113–114
    restaurants 101, 104, 114, 115, 121, 126, 127
    weddings 34
    see also difficult situations; holidays
speech
    acoustics and 73
    banana 22
    factors contributing to difficulty in understanding 90–91
    sounds 22
    ways of improving communication 91–92
    see also conversations
speechreading *see* lipreading
STAGETEXT 79
stapedectomy 14
stapes 13, 18*n*
stirrup *see* stapes
Stone, Howard E 'Rocky' 34
stress 33–34, 34
stroke causing hearing loss 17
STT *see* verbatim speech to text reporting
student guidelines for getting support 108, 154
subtitles 79–80
symbolic level of sound 63, 64

T

technology
    access to 77–81
    limitations 37
    problems with 83–84
telecommunication 124
telephone 83–89
    advantages 88
    aids for 124
    alerting systems 123
    alternatives to 84, 88–89
    attachments 86
    disadvantages 88
    emergencies 84–85